What the press says about Harlequin Romances…

"…clean, wholesome fiction…always with an upbeat, happy ending."
—*San Francisco Chronicle*

"…a work of art."
—*The Globe & Mail*, Toronto

"Nothing quite like it has happened since *Gone With the Wind*…"
—*Los Angeles Times*

"…among the top ten…"
—*International Herald-Tribune*, Paris

"Women have come to trust these clean, easy-to-read love stories about contemporary people, set in exciting foreign places."
—*Best Sellers*, New York

OTHER
Harlequin Romances
by MARGARET WAY

The Wild Swan

by

MARGARET WAY

Harlequin Books

TORONTO • LONDON • NEW YORK • AMSTERDAM • SYDNEY

Original hardcover edition published in 1978
by Mills & Boon Limited

ISBN 0-373-02188-7

Harlequin edition published August 1978

PRINTED IN U.S.A.

CHAPTER ONE

FROM every branch the great black cockatoos peered down at her, their crests rising like flames, their strong black beaks ready to strip the bark from the trees or to start the search for fat beetles and grubs. It was early morning and their hoarse chatter had awoken her.

She lay quietly, just where she was, looking back at them. The birds were her friends. Her only friends. The birds and the animals, the wild hearkening bush and the river. The dawn wind, cool and refreshing, touched her cheeks and ruffled her short curls, black as a swan's shining wings. Her fire that had burnt brightly the night before had long since gone out.

She was exhausted but quite without fear. They might come to get her, but they would never find her—Ryan, the mighty hunter, Jeff or Christy. They would never think to look for her here. The area around Djangga had never been one of their favourite haunts. Over it hung a spell and an ancient legend. Even hardened stockmen found something strange and sinister about the place, but this terrible morning it didn't bother Kylie. Nothing much mattered any more, except defeating Ryan.

Above the dark green of the trees, the budgerigars in their thousands were winging their way in their curious slanting formation to the waterholes and lagoons. The sky was still a misty pearl tinged with streaks of lemon and rose pink. Morning in the bush

was unbelievably beautiful and she lay there in intense
meditation watching the flashing little birds. There
was a swamp somewhere near her. At fifteen she knew
her bushcraft. She was almost an expert. She knew
how to live off the land. Her father had taught her.

This morning the thought of her father didn't
bother her; she was in a deep state of shock. The
violent storm of emotion had passed and again she was
quiet. When her strength returned she would move
swiftly to the top of the great monolith. The trees that
stood guard all around her were heavy with blossom
and scent; the acacias, the cassias and the bauhinias in
full bloom, their branches stripped of leaves, covered
in flowers like tropical orchids. They were supposed to
be good spirits. If they were she was fortunate to be
surrounded by some kind of magic. She would need it
to keep away the creeping horror of memory.

The wind swept firmly across her body. In another
hour the sun would have rolled all those pastel clouds
away, lighting the world with its terrible power. She
would have to fashion some kind of protection for her
head. She was fearfully tired, drained out. She lifted
her thin young arms to the heavens in a mute appeal
for help. She was thirsting for water and water was
about a mile away. Just before nightfall she had eaten
some wild fruit and drunk from a billabong of fresh,
still water. When she had found it she had been
exultant. Now she sat up and cradled her slight supple
body with her arms, hugging herself in a futile bid for
comfort.

There was none. This was Sovereign River, the
stronghold of the Langtons, and their power was
great. For an instant a great hate swallowed her up in

its maw, then she sank back into torpor. It was time to move on. This place wouldn't conceal her for ever. They might have seen the smoke from her fire. She had needed it for warmth and to keep the dingoes away. On her feet, she found herself swaying and she smiled rather foolishly. She couldn't feel ill now. Ryan would track her down, forcing her to go back. In the old days he would probably have thrown her to the lions like a Roman emperor. In this part of the world Ryan had rights over everyone. *Her* life, what was left of it, was her own.

She twisted up and brushed herself down, every muscle aching in protest. Through the trees she saw something and her heart gave a leap of fear. It seemed to wrap itself round her. She bent and picked up a jagged rock, eyes piercing the thick blanket of trees. It could be a black on walkabout, a young buck, perhaps. Her hand tightened around the rock, then she saw them more clearly—two full-grown dingoes, tawny yellow in colour, tongues lolling, watching her with bright eyes. She braced herself, drew a deep breath and hurled the rock with a boy's accuracy. The dingoes twisted around and slashed through the trees, but she knew they would follow her. She waited for a moment, then took off with a new urgency, climbing higher and higher, the physical energy the ascent required mercifully dulling the tumult in her mind. Her small feet were swift and she moved on for a long time until the sun shone over the land with a hard brilliance and the sky was a dense opal blue. Blue, like Ryan's eyes. She was shocked by the savagery of her thoughts, and she stared up at the dome above her.

A kangaroo with a joey in its pouch hopped almost

directly in front of her, staring at her with mild
inquiring eyes, and she only hoped it could smell
dingo on the wind. The hunter and the hunted. She
showed her teeth in a bitter little smile. The sun
gathering force made her hair cling in black silky
whorls to her temples and cheeks where the heat beat
in dusky patches. Her shirt was torn and every part of
her girl-into-woman's body was aching, her tilted eyes
half glazed with shock and exhaustion. The heat even
in spring was a pitiless glare, every last shadow, every
patch of shade eaten up in the sun's awful splendour.

It would be a year of drought. The signs showed.
But no drought would ever wear down Sovereign
River. It was indomitable and its lust for human
sacrifice could never be denied. Kylie shook her head,
muttering to herself incoherently. A great wedge-
tailed eagle coasted over her and she clapped her
hands in a flurry of sound. It too was after the joey.
She shivered and her young shoulders sagged. Sur-
vival was the name of the game and no small thing was
safe. She rested against a boulder, wiping the blue sea
of mirage out of her eyes. From this vantage point she
could see the silver streak of billabong from the night
before. A great yearning came on her for a drink of
water. Water was life and nowhere more than the
great Outback. Her clear olive skin was tanned to gold,
but there was no mistaking the effect of the sun on her
head. She would have to seek shelter.

A dry rustling near her betrayed the presence of a
snake. There were snakes and lizards everywhere. She
moved carefully over the stones so as not to disturb it.
They no more wanted trouble than she did. She
stopped, startled, mindful of fangs. The snake raised

its cruel triangular head and looked into her face, but again she knew no fear. It could strike her now and she could die an awful death here in the wilderness, but she didn't care. The one person in the world she loved and who loved her was gone. It lent her a massive indifference, and the snake, recognising her condition, uncoiled its long length and slid away into the rocks. The sweat had broken out on her head. The natives worshipped the snake. There were great ritual snakes drawn all over the saves on the desert side of the Run.

From a great distance sounded a series of gunshots and she started visibly, the effect on her extraordinary. A frantic light came into her eyes and she dug in her heels, remembering all she had learnt about the art of concealment. There were many men to track her— men, horses, even the helicopter. She had seen it making great sweeps of the bush the day before. In her shock and intolerable distress the Langtons had taken on the role of hunters, never rescuers. And Ryan she feared above all. It would be a nightmare fight to escape Ryan. He would search for her for ever. Every last one of them on the station, man, woman and child, had to be accounted for. Bitterly she reflected on her father's unswerving allegiance to the Langtons, his special feeling for Ryan. She too had gone in awe of him, but never again. The shy, unquestioning hero-worship of a young girl had changed to a ferocious hate. Jeff and Christy were different. They didn't count. This was Ryan's world, and she didn't want to survive on it.

There were already three of her family's graves on the property, for the great stations buried their own.

Her mother had died when Kylie was nine, taking with her the long-awaited infant son, Martyn. The grief of it was still with her. After that, though her father clung to her and needed her, he had to send her away to her boarding school in Brisbane, but both of them lived for vacation time when she was flown back to the station. This time Ryan, in Brisbane for a conference, had even called to the school to collect her. How the other girls had envied her, wild with their comments. Sovereign River was no ordinary place and Ryan Langton was no ordinary man, but the owner of a vast cattle station, one of the country's aristocrats, a member of the powerful landed gentry, head of a great pioneering family. Crimson-cheeked and excited she had even basked in the reflected glory, but never again. The pride that had blazed in her had turned to an equally passionate hate.

Not that any of them would care. She was a young person of no importance. The Langtons had always been kind to her in their condescending fashion, but she could never be one of them, never for one moment top drawer. Ryan's sister, Claudia, home too from her exclusive establishment, always tried to close the door on her, but the younger boys and the coolly gracious Mrs Langton took an interest in her. Ryan was the one apart. Law on the station, his power was enormous.

Only once had Kylie seen his superb arrogance shaken. The scene was scorched into her mind. Her father's death had been the worst tragedy on the station in over a decade. The shock had been ravishing, bringing her to breaking point. She couldn't for one moment feel pity for Ryan. Answerable to Ryan in all things, her father could never have disobeyed instructions about getting rid of the wild stallion, though the staff to a man had closed ranks against her stricken accusations. She had flown at Ryan in a screaming rage, calling him: 'Murderer!' and he had held her in the way nobody had ever held her, his blue eyes blazing lightning, his grim face compassionate, but she had never seen that.

Later she had been taken to the Big House and folded into the most beautiful bed she had ever slept in in her life. Mrs Langton, the least demonstrative of women, had even kissed her and brushed back her hair, with Claudia for once looking at her with something approaching kindness, but it was Ryan's probing eyes she had to escape. He could read her mind.

She had waited the days quietly, gathering herself in preparing her plans, then she had ridden out with her dear old Lucy, sending the mare back on home after she had reached a definite point of no return. The rest of the way she had covered on foot. Wild terrain but unfailingly beautiful, a sea of blossoming bush. None of her thoughts had coherence. She had no real idea what she was doing. Life had suddenly become an intolerable nightmare, but she would survive without the Langtons or die on ceremonial ground a few desperate miles from her mother and father and Martyn.

Despite this death wish, she fashioned with infinite patience a protective headdress of shiny linked leaves that framed her innocent, heartbreaking little face. Life hadn't handed her any prizes, but she never thought of it like that. Because it seemed important to repay her father's loving pride in her, she had become a very good student, earning excellent reports, but as soon as she was through the final grade there was only one ambition she had ever had; to look after her father, the dearest, most unselfish man there ever was. His loss and the tragic circumstances that surrounded it devastated her mind and accounted for her present condition. Fifteen, nearly sixteen was a difficult age for the getting of wisdom.

She looked back, staring about her wondering if the dingoes were still following her with their silent menace. Higher up she would be safe. She would bury herself in this ancient shrine and damn Ryan Langton, damn Sovereign River. Damn the lot of them! She was filled with a burning desire to hide from the world. Stricken and heartbroken, she kept going, but eventually had to stop to rest.

By late afternoon Kylie was staggering, her strength depleted. She almost passed the entrance to a cave, saw it just in time and came back to check it, pulling away the vegetation from the semi-circular opening. Dust and leaves whirled around her face and a goanna ran at her at full tilt. She backed, fell over and rolled, sliding down the rough earth. Clumps of saltbush stopped her, but she felt her fright very definitely.

The light was nearly gone when she heard her name called. She waited to make sure it hadn't been a figment of her imagination. It had been a hard day. It came again and she froze like a wild creature, debating her best course of action. She knew that voice; she would know it anywhere. Her eyes were enormous and almost mindless with panic. He *mustn't* find her. Her face under the sunburn was ashen, but she stiffened her body, ignoring all the stabbing pains of overstrained muscles. Action was imperative. Not so far above her Djangga, like a pagan temple, was still burnished in gold. If she could only reach it . . .

Desperately praying, she lurched over the jagged slopes, missed her footing and swung out precariously. Sweat had broken out all over her body, making it harder for her to retain her hand-holds. She clawed frantically, hands bleeding, clinging to the life she thought she didn't want, her teeth clenched hard on her bottom lip, when the solitary eagle shot up from the cliff face before her, spreading its massive wings, its eyes gleaming savagely.

Her fingers unclutched in sheer, startled fright. She fell noiselessly, her slight body plummeting to a narrow ledge below. Djangga *did* possess some power of evil. It was the last thought of her conscious mind before blackness received her on a mighty wave.

CHAPTER TWO

WHEN Kylie came back to full consciousness she realised the man standing above her was Ryan. Whatever she did, he found her just the same. Too helpless, too beaten for words, she just lay there like a crumpled doll looking up at him, impaled by those blazing blue eyes. No one was more perfectly cut out to throw a long shadow than Ryan Langton. Desperately she tried to turn her head, withdrawing her arm from the branch of a sapling ghost gum that had miraculously cushioned and broken her fall.

His voice reached her with a terrible urgency, its dark vibrancy almost rasping. 'Lie still, Kylie—perfectly still. You can't do anything for yourself. Wait until I reach you!'

'Go away!' she said, on a hoarse little whisper.

His laugh was short and she feared it. 'Don't talk!'

Though the slope was murderous he was coming right down to her and she could recognise the steel in him. The tall lean body rippled with grace and her eyes clung to him as though hypnotised. He was feeding out a double thickness of rope anchored strongly somewhere above him, but even so she knew he was in danger. Beyond them was a drop of a hundred feet or more, and she didn't care about that either. She had only to thrust her body a little to the left to go over the edge.

A branch of the ghost gum shot out in a coil and she heard his warning hiss of breath. 'Keep still, Kylie. For God's sake do as I tell you!'

'Why don't you go away and leave me!' she said wretchedly. 'If I go, you'll come with me!'

'Little fool!' he returned rather savagely. It had been a frightful, wearying day for him too, full of stress and nameless dreads. He more than anyone knew how Kylie had idolised her father.

'Jolly decent of you!' she was saying solemnly, hating him and hating him, longing to wax sarcastic but showing distinct signs of fainting.

Then he was there, bending over her, tracing her body with sure hands, risking his life on the narrow crumbling ledge that had supported no more than the ghost gum.

Her dark eyes were almost black with pain. 'How

did you find me? I thought it would be like looking for a needle in a haystack!'

'It would be just like you to lose yourself on Djangga!' His hands examined a deep scratch and she winced. 'I don't know how you found the strength to push on. There's nothing of you but enormous eyes!'

'And I hope they scare you!' she said bitterly.

'Oh, they do!' Abruptly he glanced back at her. 'Are you in any pain?'

'My head and my ankle.'

'You've given us hell!' His dark face tightened.

'Why, because I'm not dead?'

'You've been doing your best,' he snapped.

'It was fun. Why did you come after me?'

'The best of friends should never part!'

'*Friends*—my God!' She made a sudden violent movement away from him and he seized her up in his strong arms, hurling them both backwards. Rocks and dust and flying leaves whipped all around them and Kylie cried out with the urgency of the moment, her slight body crushed against him, biting her lip against the fiery pain in her ankle. For a moment she thought she would faint with the pain.

His muffled violent oath cleared her head. He was holding her painfully close so that she had to clamp her teeth against all the burning sensations that were invading her body. The earth beneath them was vibrating and when she opened her eyes, the sapling had disappeared and she could see down into the heavily timbered valley.

'Dear God!'

It wasn't what she had planned precisely and her trembling body shook with silent, bitter laughter.

With her father gone there was no one to regret her death, but what a furore there would be if she took with her the master of Sovereign River.

'One false move and I'll kill you myself!' Ryan said violently.

'How delightful! Murderer. *Murderer!*'

'Go on, hate me, little savage. It will keep you alive!'

They were locked in a terrible embrace and she found his touch shockingly repugnant, making the hot blood race through her veins. His voice was very soft, filled with a terrible menace. 'I'm going to loop this rope around your waist and you're going to help me. I know your ankle is giving you hell, but you're not going to faint or give me any more dramatics. You have to remain conscious while I pull us up the cliff face!'

She turned up her face, her enormous dark eyes filled with loathing. 'I wonder if I could!' she said oddly.

'Kill us both?'

'Why not?' Despite herself her eyes filled with tears. 'I've nothing to live for except maybe vengeance!'

The rope rasped her bare skin, but she kept her eyes on Ryan's face. He was tensely alert, his lean powerful body in superb condition. Even so, in a minute she could destroy them.

'You want to, Kylie, but you can't. You're coming with me. You're going to get right back in there in life's arena and justify the extravagant pride your father had in you.'

'I hate you!' she said with no pang of gratitude.

'Maybe you were meant to!' he muttered, and his blue eyes briefly touched her. 'Just don't let it drive you to insanity. I'm going to get us both off this ledge. You'll have to climb on my back and hold on just as hard as you know how. Pretend you're trying to strangle me.'

'All right!' she said shortly.

'Good. This is it!'

He bent and took her slight body, but when he stood up her ankle was jolted and pain rushed through her body like a flame. 'I can't do it!' she cried, and she sounded like a child.

'You can and you *will*. You've come this far. Take your mind off your ankle. Keep thinking of how you're going to spend your life making me pay!'

The handsome dark face looked faintly harassed and impossibly Kylie smiled. 'I'm ready when you are!'

The muscles of her stomach contracted and she thrust the side of her face against the width of his back, useless to help him, only a burden. Though he was splendidly fit and her own body was registering his abundant vitality he had to be feeling her dead weight against him as he kicked up the rock face. It was slow going and every moment the menace seemed to increase.

By the time they reached safety the strength had run out of her. It was terribly quiet and almost foreboding, and she lay where Ryan left her until the swirling mists around her head cleared. Her small upturned face was very lovely, very still and very tragic. Ryan was looking down at the ledge that could have been their death trap and when he came back to

her Kylie had to set her mind to concentrate on what
he was saying.

'We'll have to wait until morning to descend!' he
said rather curtly, his black brows drawn together.
'I'm going to fire off three shots to let them know I've
found you—and alive. The boys have been nearly out
of their minds with anxiety!'

She gave a little whimpering laugh that was like a
tinkle of silver in the silence. 'I'm sorry. It would be
too much to upset *you*!'

He shrugged and said levelly, 'Try to relax. You
look absolutely spent. How young you are, Kylie!'

'I'd like to be dead.'

'I realise that!' he said harshly, 'but I have strong
personal reasons for wanting you around!'

'Really?' She sat up shakily and glanced around
her. 'Won't you bore me with the details?'

'You'll just have to wait!' He walked off a few paces
and fired the shots that reverberated around the silent
hills marking the remote spot and letting the search
party know Kylie had been found safe and sound.

A rush of nervousness made her thrust her hand
through her curls, rippling silkily around the collar of
her torn shirt. The scratch on her collarbone still
smarted from his hands and she could feel the sun
burn on her cheekbones and the bridge of her nose.
There was a strange drawing power about Ryan's tall
figure, a compelling inherent authority that flowed
around him. Such a wave of bitterness swept through
her that she was powerless against it. How could she
hope to defeat such a man?

He swung about and gave her a piercing glance.
'We'll make it up there to Djangga for the night.

You're tired. So am I. Let's get going!'

'Not me!' she said grimly. 'I won't be moving for a long time.'

For answer he simply gathered her up as though she weighed no more than a leaf and her arms slid around his neck because she couldn't afford to struggle. Shock and pain were combining to lessen her fury and her slight, bruised body turned fluid.

'You're very lucky I don't beat you!' he said tersely. 'You deserve it!'

Her body jerked convulsively and his grip tightened, biting into her. 'Don't think for one moment I'm going to thank you!'

'No,' he silenced her. 'You've got plenty of courage, Kylie, but you're a damned nuisance!'

'I feel the same way about you!'

Unexpectedly he gave a soft laugh in his throat that wasn't echoed in his blue, heavily lashed eyes. Even so it made her catch her breath, adding some new, inexplicable tension. She gave him a wary glance, wishing with all her heart she could walk and he didn't have to carry her. She had never been remotely so close to him before and she found herself in a turmoil. Female-like, she noticed the clean bronze polish of his skin, the cool hard mouth chiselled with frightening perfection. No other member of his family had the depth of colour of his eyes or their impatient brilliance. They were all of them handsome, but Ryan was arresting, with the same look of arrogance and good blood his thoroughbreds wore. She scanned his jawline and his hard chin and he dropped his dark head and looked into her eyes.

'Think you'll know me again?'

'I'm sure I'd know you any place in the world.'

'I'm not really the devil!' he replied.

She tried vainly to reason with her curious response and even tried to twist herself out of his arms.

'You're making a mistake, Kylie!' he said, and she stopped, her resistance ebbing abruptly. He bore her upwards with him to the great dome-shaped rock the natives called Djangga, setting her down gently just inside the main cave. Her ankle was throbbing, but so overpowering was his effect on her that she didn't mention it, but watched him collect enough material to get a fire going.

It sprang up with a crackle, flaring brilliantly, bringing to life all the rock drawings around the wall and the ceiling; human beings, animals, trees, abstract symbols, one like a god wearing a concentric circle for a head and a monstrous creature like a crocodile, a thousand miles from the jungle rivers and swamps. For a moment Kylie was so fascinated, so dominated by the hard clearness of these ancient relics that she tried to stand up. Pain took her breath and plunged her into the whirlpool of darkness again. A hard encircling arm came around her and she heard him saying sharply, 'You're having difficulty with that ankle, aren't you? Let me have another look at it.'

She slid down to the ground again and he moved close to her, easing the sneaker loose, frowning at the swollen joint. She shut her eyes all the time he explored it, surprised at the pleasure it gave her not to allow one small gasp of pain or self-pity to escape her.

'You're lucky you came out of it with only this!' he murmured brutally, though his hands were tender.

'So are you!'

'You wouldn't have done it, Kylie!'

'Maybe not,' she agreed quietly. 'There are other ways to make you pay!'

'Then you'd better wait until you're a woman!' His blue eyes mocked her and after a minute he got to his feet and stripped off his shirt, tearing a long continuous piece around the hem.

It was hard *not* to look at him. He was facing her and the firelight was rippling over bone and muscle, the taut polished skin, the dark tangle of hair on his hard, wide chest. He was very lean and perfectly proportioned and it was almost unendurable to have to sit there feeling so daunted without quite knowing why. She had always known he was an exceptionally handsome man, not, it seemed, most cruelly illuminated despite her youth and innocence.

He didn't even glance at her, just bent once more to tend her injured ankle. When it was over, her breath was coming fast. 'Why worry about me?' she said jaggedly. 'You've never had time for your lowliest subject before!'

'Let me tell you I've noticed you plenty of times.'

She looked at him in surprise, finding his brilliant gaze riveting. 'Just imagine, I never knew!'

'Does it comfort you now that you do?'

'On the contrary, I hate you,' she said flatly.

'How you enjoy it!'

'And it will last for ever!'

He shrugged and moved away from her. 'For ever is a long time, little one. Don't be too hard on me.'

'I just wanted you to know!' she said, disappointed by his indifference.

He glanced back at her abruptly, his eyes full of

irony. 'And what are your reasons?'

'You know!' Her black eyes filled with tears and she brushed them away sharply.

'Only a female could be so appallingly cruel!'

'Yes,' she said, 'and I plan to keep on reminding you. You could have handled it all differently. You've been making decisions all your life. You chose to save me, now I'll cause serious trouble if I can!'

'Your intentions, like the rest of you, I see clearly!' He stooped swiftly and threw another branch on the fire, then he stood tall, stretching his arms above his head and relaxing his head. 'God, what an undeserved day!'

'Forgive me!' Her tender mouth thinned.

'I *do*, because you're a child!'

'Not because I'm so recently bereaved!' she said roughly. 'I'll never forget how Dad died. Never, never, to the last day of my life.'

'Well, come to that, I won't forget either. Keep that in your mind, little girl!' He reached for his discarded shirt and put it on again, leaving it hanging open rakishly. Cold air was already seeping in through the mouth of the cave, making the fire dance. 'All I've got to offer you is a chocolate!'

'I don't want it!' she said decisively.

Something about his eyes frightened her. 'Eat it!' he said in a voice that brooked no argument, taking a small block out of his breast pocket and passing it to her.

'What are you going to have?' she asked before she could help herself.

'How good of you to think of me, Kylie!'

She looked up at his mocking, intelligent eyes and

for an instant the impulse to fling the chocolate back at him was too powerful to restrain. She tipped her face up and hurled it, and he caught it in mid-flight.

'You're a little primitive, do you know that?' His blue eyes narrowed and a sharp thrill cut through her. 'There's a time and place for everything, Kylie. I don't want any more now of your hostility. Just finish the chocolate and try to get some rest!'

She continued to contemplate him speechlessly, her great eyes burning. 'If you say so, Mr Langton. You're the Great Man!'

'Well, yes. In this part of the world, anyway. I know you've always disliked it.' He was smiling faintly, but somehow he looked very male and dangerous.

Kylie sat there with her back resting against the granite wall, feeling baffled and betrayed. Her small face might have been carved out of ivory. She was so hungry it was too much of a struggle not to eat the chocolate. Once she looked up to catch the blue eyes flicking her and and she saved a small wedge and held it up to him like an offering.

He took it and his fingers brushed her own. 'That was a convincing display of hunger, so I appreciate the gesture. Thanks, Kylie. Are you sure you feel all right?'

She took a deep swallow, excited by her recklessness. 'You're very solicitous for a *murderer*!'

He spun around so quickly she slammed her back into the granite wall. He came to her, dropped down beside her and took her slender arms in a vice. 'Never say that to me again!'

'It bothers you, does it?' The tears started to slide

exhaustedly down her cheeks. 'Do you think I care if I hurt you? I almost wanted to *kill* you back there on the ledge!'

'You know why? You're shocked out of your wits!'

'You could have saved him!'

Such a wealth of despair was in her voice he twisted around and pulled her sideways into his arms. 'Cry, Kylie. Drive the rage out of you. What you're saying is senseless and cruel!'

He was grasping her shoulders and she brought her own hand up to push him away. 'Stallions can be broken to the saddle!'

'It's often too dangerous. Faith in a rogue is one thing you can't afford. I told your father to get rid of it. It could never be broken. I knew its destructive power the first time it was brought into the yards. Listen to me, Kylie!'

She shook her shiny dark head, the pain in her heart appalling. For a moment she was back in the yards and the whole horrific scene unfolded again. She heard the shot. She smelt the blood. The beloved familiar figure lay face down on the sand, the felled stallion brought down by the fence. Christy was there, being violently ill, and Ryan held the gun. She had flung herself at him at a screaming run, calling him names so unchildlike, so full of hatred it burst like a bubble in her brain.

'I can't bear it!' she said, her heart racing under his hand, her expression heart breaking.

'I know how you feel!'

'Oh, bless you!' She laughed and the sound jarred him badly.

'Be still, Kylie. You won't arrive at any logical thought until you're still and quiet.'

Her black head jerked up and she was very pale. 'I don't want any of this. I don't want you to hold me.'

'My dear, it would be cruel to let you go!'

His voice was very quiet and she turned her tear-stained face away. 'I'm not a child!'

'No, you're not!' he said finally. 'Not in the least!' Abruptly he released her and stood up. 'Try to get some sleep. We'll leave at first light.'

Her tone matched his curtness. 'I won't go back to your family. I'm not one of them. I'm not even fit to breathe the same air!'

'An opinion you've expressed only too often!' His finely chiselled mouth was ironic.

'I have some rights after all. I'll never live in the same place as you Langtons and I won't accept your charity!'

'What *will* you do?' he asked a little cruelly. 'Fifteen, nearly sixteen. Who is there to hold on to?'

'Never you. I won't accept charity from you!'

Her young voice held a touch of torment and he found it easy to lie. 'You won't have to!' he said with sharp simplicity. 'Your father provided adequately for you. He's been putting aside money for years. In fact he discussed your future with me many times over. He adored you and he wanted the best for you. I know a lot more about you than you think. I know you're a clever girl and you can conduct yourself like a lady. I know you have plenty of courage even if it's all the wrong kind. Who else would ever dare to say what you've said and get away with it?'

'Go on.' She looked acutely into his face as though searching out the real truth. 'Did Dad really provide for me?'

'I don't lie!' he said suavely. 'You won't be rich, but you won't have to ask anyone for anything until you're of an age to support yourself.'

She sighed and moistened her soft, moulded mouth. 'And that's the truth?'

'So help me!'

She stared at her bandaged ankle and twisted about more comfortably. 'I'll do everything my father expected of me, but nothing will ever change between us!'

'You're talking nonsense!' he said with open arrogance.

'No. I'll always remember there's a grave between us.'

His dark face tightened in hard disgust. 'You know damned little after all. I can't talk to you now, Kylie. I can only ignore you. You've arranged yourself as best you can. Close your eyes!'

'I might as well while I've got the chance!' She gave a little moody shrug and then winced.

'What is it, your ankle?'

'My head!'

'I suppose you could have a light concussion.' His eyes brooded on her pale, confused face as if she were something under a microscope.

Kylie regretted having spoken at all. He was making her nervous in a way she could never have believed. Even the sight of him was like a knife twisting inside her. Once she had thought him god-like and she couldn't entirely chase the aura away. Or perhaps it was just that he was Ryan Langton, master of Sovereign River, and that was enough. There was no point in talking anyway, and she was tired … tired … tired. It had been a long, hard day. The trouble was she was cold.

'Of course you are!' he said, and she realised she had spoken when she thought her lips were clamped shut. His shadow against the cave wall was fantastically tall. 'You should have remembered the desert grows cold at night.'

'I didn't think about it at the time. What about you? You've made a mess of your shirt.'

'That doesn't matter, I'm tough!' He turned with lithe swiftness and threw another armful of dried-out mulga branches on the fire. It was obvious that natives had used the cave for protection and warmth because neat bundles of firewood were piled up against the end wall. The flames licked up in an orange arc and danced wildly, piercing the purple shadows and lighting the totem figures and symbols so that they seemed to leap from the wall. The god figure with the concentric head focused his round eyes on them and Kylie gave a breathy little laugh, her heart drumming.

'Who's he supposed to be?'

'God knows!' Ryan answered offhandedly, 'but we've tracked him to his lair. Don't work yourself into a frenzy. For all we know we might have his approval.'

'You dare to think so?' She stared up at his tall figure.

'Someone outside of me was pretty anxious to save your life!' he pointed out dryly. 'Without that ghost gum you'd have gone right over into the valley.'

'And taken you with me.'

'I'm thankful you didn't!' He returned her burning gaze coolly. 'Did you really have to do it, Kylie? You must be lacerated all over.'

'My hands have stopped bleeding,' she said, at last.

'And you weren't frightened?'

'Of course not. Everything seemed to want to leave me alone. Except you.'

'You couldn't possibly get away. Not on Sovereign River!' He glanced down at her bundled so pathetically on the cavern floor. Her denim jeans were torn. So was her cotton shirt. With a kind of repressed sympathy he walked across to her and let his hand slip over her bare arm. 'You *are* cold!'

She shivered involuntarily and with a muffled exclamation he dropped down beside her and pulled her to him a little roughly. 'Don't struggle before you think!' he warned her. 'You're cold, and I intend to warm you. You're quite safe with me.'

'I'm not afraid!' she said tautly, the touch of his hands spreading warmth right through her body.

'You'll have to do something about that almighty chip on your shoulder, Kylie, otherwise you'll be setting a pattern for the rest of your days.'

'I expect it will be hell, like it is now!' she said pointedly.

He flashed her a downwards glance from his intensely blue eyes. 'Try to sleep!' he said firmly. 'You look like a hard-pressed little rabbit, all those fearful glances chasing across your face. I'm perfectly capable of keeping watch and I don't intend to make conversation with a distressed little soul!'

'It wouldn't profit either of us anyway!' she said a

little vaguely. 'You'll know for ever what I'm thinking.'

'And I'd be very careful not to say it again. Your
only excuse is you're too bewildered to see things
clearly!'

She kicked with her good foot and tried to struggle
away. 'Oh, for God's sake!' he said with sudden
anger, and held her easily like a snapping terrier.
'Let's rest. You've got no choice.'

'I'll lie down over there.'

'Will you indeed?' He looked down his arrogant
straight nose at her. 'You'll stay right here and you'd
go straight to sleep if you'd give yourself a chance. If I
could have saved you what you've gone through I
would have. You simply walked in at the most terrible
moment you could have. There were witnesses, Kylie.
I told your father to shoot the stallion or drive it back
to the range. He was too slow to obey!'

'Dad worked all his life with horses!' she said, very
close to tears again.

'And he longed to tame that stallion. It was a
wonderful-looking animal, but it was nearly crazy in
captivity. Believe me, I told your father what to do,
but he couldn't bring himself to do it. It's as simple as
that!'

Kylie leaned her head back, her eyes filled with
pain. Her silky hair spilled over his tanned arm and
clung in tendrils to his skin. 'I promised myself I'd
make you pay!'

'I damn near did today! Close your eyes, little girl.
You're the absolute limit!'

'Don't imagine you have to feel responsible for

me!' Her eyelids were beginning to fall.

'Oh no, far from it!' He said it very nicely. He had a beautiful voice.

'Will there ever be any happiness in the world for me?' she asked, wondering what was happening to her.

'That depends on you, Kylie!' His hand was in her hair, smoothing it back from the temples. 'The first thing you have to do is trust people!'

'Never *you*!' she said drowsily. 'I know you're responsible for everything. It's no use, you see,' her voice caught on a little muffled sob. 'I can never forget!'

In the flare of the firelight his dark face looked hard and unyielding, the features marvellously chiselled. 'Bury your cold little heart, Kylie. Some day some man is going to know how to find it!'

'I doubt that!' For a moment her eyes flashed open, brilliant as jets.

'I might even reserve you for myself.'

'That's inexcusable!' she said scornfully. 'I think you should apologise!'

'Why? It's just dawned on me you're going to make a very beautiful woman!'

She drew in her breath guardedly. 'Don't amuse yourself with me, Mr Langton.'

He spoke without emphasis, but there was mockery in his voice. 'Don't panic, little one. You're hardly old enough anyway!'

'Do you think so?'

'I *know* so!' One hand moulded her delicate shoulder and held it.

The shock of feeling within her was too powerful to

withstand. She was doing violence to herself lying against him, his bush shirt swinging open carelessly to expose the bronze column of his throat and his hard, lean torso. Perhaps it was a dream, a terrible, disquietening dream. She couldn't follow the reactions of her awakening body. They were as curious as they were humiliating. She could only fear them, too young and inexperienced to guard her eyes.

'Don't look at me like that!' he said gently, almost humorously.

'I'm horribly afraid of you.' She had spoken aloud again.

'Let's hope so!' The humorous inflection was still in his voice, but his eyes glittered like sapphires.

'I couldn't possibly go to sleep in your arms!'

'I know. You've said that before!' His hand was in her hair again, softly brushing it, so gentle and relaxing it acted like a drug. 'Go to sleep, you wild and lonely little girl!'

There was a curious over-gentleness in his voice and movements as though he was quelling a more forceful reaction. 'It's amazing!' she murmured in a meaningless way. 'Amazing and . . . unthinkable!'

He laughed softly and felt the little tremble move over her body. 'Don't think about it now. It will keep!' He eased his own long limbs into a more comfortable position, cradling her protectively.

Kylie's heavy eyelashes fluttered once. She stared at him and frowned with a mixture of apprehension and bewilderment, then misery, exhaustion and this curious dark agitation took the last of her strength. She couldn't withdraw herself. It would only earn a crushing grip.

Ryan laid a restraining hand on her, feeling the tension in her elegant, nerve-ridden little body, and she groped at his sleeve.

'Peace, little one!'

'Never!'

'All right!' he continued to humour her. 'You'll feel better when you've rested. Talking's bad for you. You're dead beat, harassed to the bone!'

She sighed and the tips of her curls brushed his throat. Her eyelids were falling and a trance-like lethargy was taking control of her inch by inch. She had expected anger, instead she got this quiet in the eye of a storm, almost an unwilling tenderness. Finally she slept, as deeply, as innocently asleep as a child, her cameo face half hidden against him, no longer bothering to remember who he was or what he was. In the dim light her skin was as pale as ivory, her hair and her heavy lashes black as night.

The man stretched out his long legs, distributing her slight weight more comfortably into his arms. His own anger had collapsed and his hand moved over her hair in the same gentle rhythm. From outside the cave a night bird called out in its flight and the sound echoed strongly and sweetly inside the granite walls. Ryan's eyes travelled over the young girl lying so mutely against him, then he tilted his head back and shut his eyes.

Now and again came a violent little gust of wind through the mouth of the cave, but Kylie never felt it, snuggling closer unconsciously to warmth and security. From this day on her whole life would be changed, but Ryan Langton's influence over her life was more powerful than she knew.

CHAPTER THREE

IN the few years between fifteen and twenty, Kylie saw more of the Langtons than she ever wished. Her youth and her dependence made such a state of affairs unavoidable. Ryan, in accordance with her father's wishes, handled her affairs, and in doing so doubled and trebled her inheritance by way of investment. This she accepted without question. It was well known that the Langton interests were widely diversified and no one could guess at the extent of their fortune. Sovereign River, though their stronghold and one of the richest properties in the country, was by no means the extent of their assets. It was generally agreed in the pastoral world that they were millionaires many, many times over.

Kylie's schooling was paid for and her vacations supervised. There was even a Miss Carr, a very elegant and sophisticated lady who was somehow on the Langton payroll, to take her shopping for new clothes. But when, at seventeen, she won a scholarship to university, she chose to enter teacher training college with her closest friend Sara Anthony, and study for her degree at night. Though Sara was her complete opposite, warmly gregarious to Kylie's cool reserve, the girls were wonderfully compatible. Sara was blessed with a great quality of heart, and she had influenced Kylie and taken her under her wing, and now in this last year since her parents had semi-retired to a small farming property in the country, the two girls shared a flat and pooled their resources.

Both of them had been fortunate enough to gain positions at St Margaret's, a leading private girls' school, and the Anthonys' property in the country was the ideal place to spend every other week-end. As a family, the Anthonys were so friendly and welcoming that Kylie had gradually learned to relax her little aloof air, that was really a protective shell, but which some people found disconcerting. Not the Anthonys, however. They treated her like family and it thawed her lonely heart.

It didn't occur to Kylie that summer evening that Ryan Langton was so near. She was just putting the finishing touches to her make-up when Sara came back into the bedroom, her eyes gleaming, a warm rush of excitement in her cheeks.

'What's up with you? Have you won the lottery or something?'

'Have *you*, more like it!' Sara breathed.

'Out with it!' Satisfied, Kylie put her lipstick down.

'He's here at the door!'

Kylie was astonished. 'Heavens, you've met Mark.'

'Not Mark!' Sara's pert face was alight. 'Your *bête noir*! Why didn't you tell me he's a blooming miracle? I've never seen anyone so extravagantly classy!'

Kylie stared sightlessly back at her reflection. 'Ryan Langton?'

'The same!' Sara said, and rolled her round eyes. 'I find it extraordinary the way you've always described him. He's *gorgeous*! In fact I'm wretched I don't stand a chance.'

The words seemed to stick in Kylie's dry throat. 'Thanks, Sara. I'll be right out!'

'Take your time!' Sara said breezily, her hand on the doorknob. 'I'll keep him entertained!'

Kylie recovered enough to stand up. Ryan had never before arrived without warning. Claudia's birthday was more than a week off. These rare entries into her world upset her, for he was no less her enemy as the years passed. It was probably a business trip and he had found the odd minute to check up on her. She knew this kind of thing to be automatic with him. Ryan had always kept her under surveillance.

Her hands were gripped together and her large dark eyes were unquiet. Oh, for Sara's breezy aplomb! All contact with Ryan Langton aroused countless small agonies. Ever since that night on Djangga she had been almost rigid in his presence. Neither of them had ever mentioned it again and she had been wretchedly ill afterwards for more than a week. Perhaps in saving her life he had made an acid mark on her.

The evening out she and Sara had been planning now meant nothing whatsoever. She wished simply she was a hundred miles away instead of a door away from Ryan Langton whose thoughts and actions were quite inexplicable.

Sara's floral perfume was still in the air, a heavenly blend of roses and jasmine, exuding warmth and Sara's own fresh personality. Her own perfume worked a different magic, more erotic on her skin, but overpowered now by Sara's indulgence. She appeared to have been entranced by Ryan and she was known to be a fast worker. It was quite impossible and Kylie could have laughed aloud. Sara, like herself, was

a nobody with no recognised family tree. Sara, bright
and switched on as she was, would be no match for a
terrible woman like Elizabeth Langton, so coldly
charming, so utterly proper, despising everyone who
came out of a different mould.

Kylie halted before the long mirror, sweeping a
tense look over her appearance. It was impeccable and
it gave her a little confidence. Her whole style was
total simplicity. She was too small and slight of build
to go for magnificence anyway. Her dress, a dark red,
was the most dramatic with her skin and eyes, fluid
over her slender body and sensual too, though this
hadn't occurred to her for, of course, she didn't see
herself as others did. Her hair was still the short cap of
curls it had always been, but very much more sophisticated in style, layered right through and forming a
shiny ebony halo around her rather aloof, delicately
boned little face. She had, as Claudia had claimed, a
'foreign' look, but it was an asset in mass-produced
faces, that and the intriguing elegance, the exotic set
of her eyes and winged brows, even if occasionally
she wished for several more inches and a lovely
straight mane of tawny blonde hair like Sara. Sara was
a very vital, warm-hearted young woman and Kylie
considered herself lucky to have her for a friend. At
the same time she wondered what Sara might be saying. She was just that tiny little bit indiscreet, and
keeping her life apart from Ryan Langton infatuated
Kylie like a fever.

Sara's low gurgle of laughter carried through the
hallway. She was still laughing when Kylie walked
into their informal little sitting room with its rough
silks and linens and natural timber and cane furniture.

'Why, I'd love to!' Sara was saying, absolutely betraying herself with her supercharged face and voice.

'Then it's settled!' Ryan rose to his feet as Kylie came into the room, setting his glass down. His vivid eyes flashed over her in the old remembered way and he walked towards her with the curious grace and lean economical movements so much a part of him. 'How are you, Kylie?'

She gave him her hand, inclining her head rather like a Mandarin princess. 'I'm surprised to see you here, Ryan. I didn't even know you had this address.'

'I'm in town for a conference,' he said, smoothly avoiding an answer. 'I'm flying back the day after tomorrow. If it suits you, I'll be happy to have you aboard. It will save you a lot of chopping and changing.'

'Not to speak of the fare!' Sara chimed in gaily. 'I'd accept in a minute!'

'But I very much doubt if it could be arranged,' Kylie said in her cool little voice.

'Don't be silly!' Sara contradicted in all innocence. 'You're Annabel's little pet. Besides, there's only ten days of term left.'

Kylie flashed a speaking glance at her friend and Sara immediately jumped to her feet with considerable coltish animation. 'I'd better make myself beautiful before the doorbell rings. Kylie and I are out on a double date, as I told you. It was great meeting you, Ryan!'

'My pleasure!' he said suavely. 'And Sara, I wasn't merely being polite, you're very welcome on Sovereign River. Next time Kylie comes out to us I'd be delighted if you would join her!'

Sara flushed her pleasure, looking very young and pretty. 'Why, thank you. I can scarcely wait. Why Kylie hardly mentions you I can't imagine!'

Ryan caught Kylie's vaguely agonised expression and smiled. 'No doubt she has her reasons!'

'Well, 'bye now!' Sara waved her hand gaily. 'A great one for secrets is our little Kylie!'

'Aren't you wearing the *blue* dress?' Kylie asked her brightly.

'Sure, kid. You've got to stop being so serious—I tell her all the time. By the way, I just thought of something. Barry is going to be ten minutes late. He loves his work, that boy. Kills himself to get ahead.'

'That's the way of it!' Ryan remarked dryly.

'Stay right there until I get back!' Sara flashed him another of her brilliant smiles.

'I'm not planning on going anywhere. I'd like to see the kind of young man that interests Kylie!'

'It's the other way around!' Sara announced dramatically, and Kylie could cheerfully have flung a cushion at her. 'They all try to impress her. She's a siren. No one minds *me*!'

'That couldn't be further from the truth!' Kylie turned to look pointedly at her friend and belatedly Sara got the message. She danced away to the bedroom, leaving a lengthening pause behind her.

Kylie was unwilling to flutter around him and be charming. The sight of him was affecting her more savagely than she cared to think about. She sat down in a cane chair and Ryan took the seat opposite her. It was the supreme irony that she should see him so clearly with a woman's eye. His appearance was a frontal attack, for status and presence clung to him like a second skin.

He was dressed casually in slacks and a matching lightweight jacket, with an open-necked blue shirt in the same astonishing blue as his eyes. The effect was stunning, a relaxed arrogance in his tall, lean body. He leaned forward, forcing her to meet his eyes.

'I don't think you really answered me. How *are* you?'

'Fine. I'm grateful for the inquiry!'

'Sure you can spare the time to speak to me?'

'Of course!' She dropped her heavy lashes, wishing with all her heart she didn't feel so threatened. 'Why do you want me to come for Claudia's birthday? Will it amuse you?'

'Don't talk like that, Kylie. You know I don't like it. You're part of the family.'

Her black eyes flew to his and something in their expression made his nostrils flare. 'Haven't you learned anything in five years?'

She stiffened and an unfamiliar flush touched her skin. It was deadly, the hatred she had for him, and she could never be free of it. There was no profit in voicing it, so she said almost meekly : 'I've tried very hard to be a credit to you, surely?'

'I know that as well as you do!' he said, almost curtly.

'Then why are you so cruel?'

He looked at her very carefully as she sat there in her crimson dress. 'What a fantastic mind you have, Kylie! Are you always going to see me as someone sinister? You've persisted overlong and you're too young for bitterness. It will rob you of your beauty!'

'I'm sorry!' she said softly, suppressing her formidable anger. 'Shall we start again?'

'I'd like nothing better!'

'Then it shall be just as you wish!' She lifted her head and smiled at him, a smile curiously free of laughter but drawing his eyes to her curving, moulded mouth with a tiny velvety mole beside it.

'You little witch!' he said, reading her mind. 'You'll only finish up hurting yourself!'

It shook her a little and she let her real feelings flash through. 'You can't pretend either Claudia or your mother want me there.'

'Well, there's always Jeff and Christy. Neither of them have forgotten your last visit.'

'I'm not interested in either of your brothers!'

'Of course not!' His blue eyes openly mocked her.

'How's Rex?' she asked.

'The same as ever!' he said tersely. 'I'll tell him you were asking.'

'I'd like to see him again!' she murmured untruthfully.

'You will!' His cynical gaze was alight with malice. 'We both know he found you exciting.'

'I must confess I never noticed it.'

'I find that *extraordinary*!'

Their voices were clashing and she jumped to her feet. 'May I offer you another drink?'

He got up and came to stand beside her, towering over her petite height. 'Why don't you have one yourself? Your nerves are obviously jangled.'

'You do have that effect on me, yes!' she said tightly.

'Aren't you afraid I might retaliate one of these days?'

'I know you!' She dropped ice into the squat tumbler. 'Iron control!'

Ryan took the glass from her and went back to his seat. 'And who's the latest? Should I know?'

'Latest?' She raised her fine eyebrows that followed the tilt of her eyes.

'Mark, isn't it?' He leaned back negligently.

'Sure you haven't had the flat bugged?'

'No need!' he said, and his beautiful mouth thinned. 'How are you off for money? I can advance you something if you want to buy a new dress for the party.'

The quick anger burned in her cheeks. 'Are you trying to tell me I'll need something better than this?'

'Darling girl!' he said contemptuously, his eyes touching every little bit of her. 'I'm convinced you'd look desirable in a suit of armour. You deliberately misconstrue my meaning.'

'All the gentry will be there!' she said satirically.

'They have their value.'

'So I've discovered.'

He looked directly at her and she was aware again of the strange panic in her body. 'It should be a wonderful opportunity for you to land a rich husband!'

'I'd enjoy that!' She was quivering as though hard fingers touched her naked body.

'Not *you*!' he said dryly. 'Sara, maybe!'

She looked away from him, knowing his power now with the instincts of a grown woman. Not only was he an extremely handsome man, he had a powerful aura of sexuality and her whole body was screaming to be left alone. Still she had to carry on this cat-and-mouse parrying. 'Why wouldn't I?' she asked lightly. 'A fine collection of millionaires!'

'Such a pity I know you better than you think!'

'Then you must know I don't want to come with you!'

'But you'll come.'

'I *have* to!' she said tiredly. 'That's what we all do—obey orders.' She looked down at her legs, not even seeing their slender young perfection. 'When are you leaving?'

'I'll ring and let you know!' Ryan sounded very businesslike. 'It all depends how important these talks are, and I've been elected spokesman. Come over here.'

'No, I won't!'

He shrugged his powerful shoulders. 'How gauche you are!' He slipped his hand inside his jacket's breast pocket and withdrew a cheque book and a beautiful gold pen. 'Don't look like it's charity and you're going to fling it back in my face. This is your father's money!'

'It must have run out by now!' she said in some agitation.

'It would have had I not invested it so wisely!' he said very crisply indeed. 'Surely you know I'm considered a good business man!'

Kylie stood up trancelike, a small, graceful girl, expressing her uncertainties. 'You make it sound so——'

'Three, four hundred?' he asked, ignoring her.

'What do dresses cost these days?'

'It all depends. A fraction of that would do most of us, but then we're not from your circle, I'll admit!'

He stared up at her again with his magnificent arrogance. 'Rags on my ward's back! It would be a scandal. It's myself I'm thinking about.' He pulled a small table forward and wrote out a cheque in his black, flowing hand. When he had finished he handed it to her and as she went to take it, he pinned her fragile wrist. 'Thank you!' he admonished her.

'Bless you for your generosity!' Blood was coursing swiftly right through her veins.

'You're an arrogant little bitch. I should have turned you over my knee years ago!'

'I wouldn't recommend it!' Kylie was trying ineffectually to free herself.

'No, there are more suitable punishments for you these days!' His eyes dropped from her mouth to the shadowed cleft between her small, pointed breasts. She could have hit him, and feeling her silent rage he held her a minute longer. 'Still defiant, Kylie, after all these years?'

She stared back at his jewelled eyes and shivered, her dark eyes dominating her delicate face. 'You're a cruel brute, aren't you?'

'I've always treated *you* very gently. No need to rub your wrist like that—I never hurt you.' His eyes narrowed over her, his dark face saturnine.

She stood there bound, and suddenly the door bell rang out, ending the curious charade. She sprang away like a gazelle, tremendously relieved. Just a little of Ryan Langton exhausted her. There was even a hint of menace in his turbulent vitality.

It was Mark at the door. He bounded into the room with eyes for only her, spanning her narrow waist and lifting her gently to his height. 'Hi, beautiful!' For a moment it looked as if he was going to kiss her and Kylie tilted her head back. 'Oh, I'm sorry, I didn't know you had company!' Just as gently, Mark lowered her to the ground. 'You couldn't blame me, though, could you?' he appealed to the older man, who was watching them with sardonic interest.

Kylie introduced them, furious with Mark. He had acted so confidently, as if he were used to holding and kissing her, which he wasn't. The two men shook hands in the grand old tradition and she found herself wondering if men really needed women at all for companionship. Ryan looked superb, charming and disdainful, for Mark had immediately grasped that he was talking to *that* Langton and was showing a gratifying interest and admiration.

Kylie excused herself rather haughtily and went to find Sara in the bedroom. Sara was looking the picture of decorum sitting on the bed, her blue dress fanned about her. 'You two weren't having an argument, were you?'

'Why do you say that?' Kylie caught her pale reflection.

'Come, come, pet!' Sara chided her. 'I know that closed little expression. I wasn't listening, but I couldn't help hearing your voices. They didn't sound friendly.'

'It's a long story!'

'Tell me. I'd love to hear.'

'One of these days I might!' Kylie picked up her purse and walked ahead. 'Mark's here. You *do* look nice. I think we'll pick up Barry at his place.'

Sara looked incredulous. 'Are you in that much of a hurry? We could miss him.'

'We won't!'

'Listen, you're upset, aren't you?' Sara's smooth forehead crinkled.

Kylie turned and gazed moodily at her reflection. The flesh of her arms and neck looked like satin against the red dress. 'Does it show?'

'It doesn't do you any harm!' Sara said dryly. 'Some men go for moody dark eyes. You're too intense, pet. I'm always advising you against it.'

'Nice Sara!' Kylie looked towards her friend and sighed. 'Why can't I be more like you? Maybe I would have been with a mother and father.'

Sara lowered her eyes, touched, and the sad little moment passed. 'Gosh, I'm mad about your cattle baron!' she gave a voluptuous smile. 'I've never seen such a beautiful man. Enough to make a woman tremble.'

'He's already spoken for!'

'What a pity. Are you sure?'

'They marry their own!' Kylie said waspishly. 'It's something like royalty. It wouldn't do any good to get any ideas.'

'Why not?' Sara said impishly, and smoothed her dress over her rounded hips. 'A girl's always got hope!'

'Let's go!' Kylie said urgently, but Sara caught her arm and held her.

'No, listen. You're obviously not interested, but I am. I've not the least objection to becoming a social climber. I'd give anything to get into his set. It would be splendid. They're notoriously rich, aren't they?'

'They have all they need,' shrugged Kylie. 'Give it up, Sara. You're much better off with Barry. Better the devil you know than the devil you don't know.'

Sara's hazel eyes widened. 'You've got too bleak a view of men altogether. I've got more faith in them myself and I don't mind shoving a bit. A girl has to. Finding a husband is a very serious business, and I can't pass up a chance at a man like that. Besides, he's invited me next time you go. I think I'll go on a diet!'

'Don't. You have a beautiful figure!' Kylie glanced ruefully into Sara's sparkling eyes. 'It's not the marvellous idea you think it is. The property is fabulous, but there are other considerations. No woman would be good enough for Ryan in his mother's eyes. The only possible allegiance would be the daughter of one of the big pastoral families!'

'I'm sorry, I can't believe it!' Sara said faintly. 'He's his own man if ever I've seen one! And he knows a lot about women!'

'I never said he was a saint!'

'Not with those eyes and mouth!' Sara groaned quietly. 'Are you sure you're not interested in him yourself?'

'*No!*' Kylie looked mortally affronted.

'Simmer down. I don't know what Mummy would say. She wouldn't believe it possible. You might even need psychoanalysis!'

'You might be in need of it yourself if you ever tangle with the Langtons. We *have* to go out. We've been here long enough.'

'Let them wait for a second. This is important. He's got brothers, hasn't he?'

'They're nothing like him. Anyway, Mrs Langton is convinced every woman in sight is after all three of them.'

'I suppose she's right!' Sara said fairly.

'Just don't expect a big welcome if that's your attitude!'

'I'm going all the same!' Sara's eyes had the unblinking preoccupation of a cat.

'So be it. Then there's no point in warning you any further.'

Sarah laughed and looked into Kylie's still, ivory face. 'A girl has to have ambition. You don't expect enough out of life. You could have everything, with your looks and brains. I thought I knew you pretty well, but now I've met Ryan Langton I know I haven't even begun to get the picture. You've always given the impression that he's a positive ogre!'

Kylie turned away her shining head. 'That's the door bell now. Barry must have arrived. It will be possible for us to leave right away. Ryan upsets me. He always has and he always will.'

'Baby,' Sara said kindly, 'you sound as if your heart is encased in ice!'

'You mustn't worry about me at all!' Humour flashed in Kylie's beautiful dark eyes. 'I can't talk about Ryan Langton at all without the blood rushing to my head. Come on, let's go!'

Together they went out, Kylie, impatient, Sara refixing her radiant smile.

CHAPTER FOUR

KYLIE studied the view of the airport coming up on her side as they banked after take-off. It was mid-afternoon of a very hot day and the heat shimmered up from the ground. She eased her seat harness around her, only half listening to Ryan's conversation with the control tower. She was very glad he was an experienced pilot, but his six-eight-seater, however much it had cost him, didn't give the same ride as a 707, or the same feeling of security. She looked down the wing with a feeling of panic, swallowing on a faint taste of nausea, staring in front of her again to the instrument panel. For a moment there she had almost imagined herself sliding right through the window and down the wing.

It wasn't the first time she had been in a light aircraft, the Outback was full of zippy little aircraft, but her last trip to Sovereign River with a small charter flight had jolted her into a respectful fear. She could still remember the Cessna falling through the air like a lift out of order, then soaring up again, leaving all four of its passengers green. The thermals over the desert would be grim, plucking at light aircraft and throwing them round like toys in a giant hand.

'Relax!' said Ryan over the sound of the twin motors.

'I'm remembering the last time!'

'With Sandy?'

'It was like riding a buck jumper, only further off the ground!'

He laughed under his breath, his hands on the controls sure and strong. 'I promise you this trip won't be half so rough. The Baron's far more stable. We're climbing now to our cruising height. The updraughts won't bother us until we're descending—maybe!'

'I don't really like flying!' Kylie murmured unnecessarily.

'I love it!'

'It shows. When do you think we'll be there?'

'Well, as we've only just got our wheels up I'd say before dark. One stop over at Narghilla and that's it!'

'How's Laura?' she asked, looking at him briefly.

'As affable as always!'

'I'm surprised. You're leaving it far too long to walk her down the aisle.'

'I've never mentioned marriage!' he said suavely.

'She hasn't been in a hurry until lately. I know and she knows you're a man of burning ambition. Wouldn't a son be necessary. An heir?'

'Someone has to inherit!' he said simply. 'It's just that I baulk at marriage.'

'And there doesn't seem to be a remote possibility of finding a worthy enough candidate.'

He turned his head in his usual decisive fashion, flicking her mocking face. 'Don't sharpen your claws on me. You're in danger right this minute!'

'Not at all. I know you'll look after my safety. Actually Laura is rather nice. I like her—more than the others, anyway.'

'What about Camilla?' he asked, as though seeking her approval, his mouth twisting.

'She has an allergy, remember. She doesn't like horses.'

'Extraordinary, that! I wonder if anyone could help her?'

'Why can't you?' she asked abruptly. 'I mean, you don't expect anything of a woman but to sit around all day looking pretty!'

'That's not entirely true, Kylie!' he said dryly.

'What else do the women of your family do?'

'Hold your peace, doe-eyes!'

'You wrong them too,' she persisted defiantly. 'They should be allowed more say.'

'In what way?'

'You're rather remote from them—first your father, now you!'

Ryan appeared to consider that, looking so arrogant she knew she had overstepped the limit. 'Their interests aren't mine!' he admitted. 'I hold fast to what we've got—Sovereign River. God knows it took enough lives. I don't think it would deeply affect my mother or sister if I sold the station tomorrow!'

She turned her face to him, delicate and piquant, her dark eyes liquid with mockery. 'That would be a longed-for day for your uncle Gerald!'

'Do you think I don't know that?'

'Intriguing, isn't it?' she said. 'Everyone thinks it odd that Rex should be so jealous of you. I don't!'

'But then you deal in intrigues of your own. In fact you're as desperate as you're ravishing. I suggest you leave Rex alone. It's not sensible to encourage him.'

'Oh, why?' she asked in a sweet, amused voice, but inwardly seething.

'Because you're not safe with him.'

'What an odd thing to say!'

'Don't play act with me. It's not odd at all. There's something very greedy about Rex!'

'Your own cousin!' she exclaimed.

'I rarely think of him as that!'

'No, there's no love lost between you!'

He threw back his head, looking very hard and masculine. 'My uncle regards living on Victory Downs as a punishment. Banished from his own kingdom through a circumstance of birth, he's driven the old quarrels home to his sons—Rex in particular. There they fell on fertile ground. Rex succeeds his father in every way. I'm aware too that he's marked the kind of woman you've grown into.'

'Please tell me?' she invited, a shade bitterly.

'Why should I? You get told often enough. Rex is as aware as I am of the vengeful streak in you!'

She jerked a little forward in her shock, then burst into laughter, fixing her great innocent eyes on him. 'Why, whatever are you talking about? Vengeful—and who could I hurt?'

'You'd hurt me in any way you could!'

'There's so much to admire in you, Ryan!' she said, still keeping her eyes on him. 'You're so perceptive!'

'The fifteen-year-old hasn't vanished in the woman. Did you think it had?'

Her thick sooty lashes veiled her eyes swiftly. 'You sound as if I might want to plot against you!'

'Wouldn't you?' he asked with a daunting glance from his brilliant blue eyes.

'How could you bring yourself to ask such a question?'

'I've got things straight about you!' he answered

dryly. 'You're only twenty, but you could be two thousand, full of secrets. Leave Rex alone. A piece of advice and a warning: Rex could be ugly!'

'You sound angry,' she challenged him, angry herself. 'I don't think you understand him at all!'

'In all seriousness, Kylie, I'm warning you. You're only play-acting at treachery, but Rex is an authentic villain!'

'Pardon me, I thought you were!'

'Come, I hardly fit into that category. I had you one night in my arms and you emerged unscathed!'

'I should think so!' she said tightly.

'Rex is a rake!' he insisted.

'I find him very attractive, and he has a strong look of you.'

'Does that mean you find me attractive too?'

'You're a legend, Ryan. Won't that do? Why begrudge your cousin a little pleasure?'

'He'll hurt you, and he'll use you to score off me!'

Kylie only just managed to hold on to her temper. 'I'm not that modest that I don't know when a man is attracted to me for myself!'

'Don't lose your cool!' he gave her a faint grin. 'I've seen the lively gatherings around you, but I wouldn't exactly count on Rex's interest as normal. You're my ward and you could fit into his plans.'

'It might be interesting to try!'

'You'll get more than you bargained for. Don't delude yourself. Besides, his father expects him to marry well, and he's very obedient!'

'And I can't set myself up as a good catch?'

'Have you property to inherit? A large sum of

money? That's important. A man can only fall in love very briefly!'

'You're a ruthless breed, aren't you?' she said bitterly.

'Have I treated you badly?'

'Maybe even you can feel remorse!'

'I'd die for you, Kylie, isn't that something?' His blue eyes were sardonic and eventually freed her. 'It's also my job to protect you from yourself!'

'Would you know how to?'

'Indeed I do. Maybe your impulses towards self-destruction will become fewer and fewer!'

She forced her eyes away from him to look out of the window. She would never forgive or forget. Many a night she had wept into her pillow with no one to comfort her. She had been lonely for so long for someone of her own, someone of her own blood to talk to. The years of boarding school had filled her with misery despite her achievements. She had made some good friends and often been taken under a maternal wing, sharing holidays and family fun, but never *one* of them. Many people had been kind to her, but no one could take her father's place. Sovereign River had denied her his loving presence and support.

'What are you thinking about?' Ryan asked clearly, and she came back to distraught life.

'My father!' she said, and found pleasure in making his eyes glitter.

'There could be an unforeseen ending to all this, Kylie—have you considered that?'

'You may go in for dampened emotions, I don't!'

'But there's no recognition of me, the man, in you.

You only see me as Sovereign River, the fear and the danger that carried off your father.'

'That's it, I'm afraid!' she murmured, barely above a whisper.

'Then you haven't yet grown up!'

'Neither have I outgrown my nightmares. It's not a question of age but of purpose!'

'And yours doesn't falter. It goes on like the River. It might be because you were such a solitary child. All your feelings gathered and centred on your father, the one person in your life!'

'If you don't mind, I don't want to talk about it!' she snapped.

'Neither do I!' he said shortly. 'You introduced the subject. It's considered unusual to regard one's ward with distrust. Tell me, who's your quarry?'

She avoided the blue infinity of his eyes. 'It should be easy, shouldn't it?'

'I daresay, if we're talking about Jeff and Christy.'

Kylie seemed to relax a little. 'It would be a kind of bush justice to take a little of Sovereign River.'

'Only it belongs to *me*.'

'That's true, but I prefer Christy, or even Rex. Doesn't it worry you having so many people desirous of your property? You have so much responsibility, so much power and money. You work hard, yet if you were struck down tomorrow I think your loving family would settle up the estate as quickly as your lawyers could handle it, then move to a life of luxury in the city. They might even sell out to your uncle.'

His glance struck her. 'You're a cruel little thing, aren't you? Indifferent to all other pain but your own. Does it give you some kind of satisfaction to lacerate

me? My uncle Gerald would have to give up everything he possessed and then borrow, and he still
wouldn't have half enough!'

'Oh, I'm sure they would come to some arrange-
ment. You know, *family*. Your mother would think
that was only natural. After all, Sovereign River has
been the Langton stronghold since the early days!'

'But nothing is going to happen to me, Kylie. I
know the dangers. That would make it all too easy for
everyone. Besides, if there are going to be any accidents, why not today, while you're with me? I could
dispose of one of my enemies!'

She shuddered perceptibly, feeling the first stirring
of unease. 'You're joking!'

'You may not be the only lunatic with a grievance!'
he pointed out.

Put like that it sounded horrible. 'Is that how you
think of me?' she asked plaintively.

'No, like your father you remind me of a gleaming
black swan. You should stay where you belong, looking beautiful and aloof, and not mistake the wilderness
for the reaches of the River!'

'I'll keep that in mind!' she said faintly.

'And sheath your claws while you're at it. I've been
very patient!'

'But you've such a thick skin!'

'Yes, fortunately. Water off a duck's back for the
best part of five years. I wish you'd tell me what
you've been doing instead of trying to frighten me to
death!'

'Have I been doing that?' she asked.

'It's a kind of enthralment, black magic. Only your
look of vulnerability saves you. It tends to knock me

sideways just when I'm about to give you a little of what you deserve!'

'I'm surprised you hold back!' she said recklessly. 'You love domination!'

'I may change my mind!'

She glanced quickly at his dark profile and something about it made her heart lurch to a standstill. Seen like that he was almost the complete coin image of his father, handsome and intimidating, spilling out authority. The old agonies gnawed into her, bitter and corrosive.

'What are you looking for?' Ryan asked her, and just for a moment turned his face to her.

'Oh, cruelty, somewhere!' she said in a strange little voice.

She couldn't find it. Not in the eyes or the flare of the nostrils, the rest of his mouth and chin. It was a striking face, strength predominant, adding a powerful dimension to clean-cut chiselled features. His mouth, as Sara had pointed out, *was* beautiful. Much too good for him.

'Why aren't you a simple, straightforward girl?' he asked dryly.

'I used to be,' said Kylie.

'I don't think so. Even as a child you were full of temperament, an urgent little thing unwilling to give your trust or your friendship.'

'To whom could I give it other than my father and mother? My mother moved so quietly out of our lives. It unsettles me to think of her.'

'Yet you resemble neither of them, your father or your mother. In fact, your looks are quite uncommon!'

'I agree!' She tugged at her short curls impatiently. 'I think I'd like to have long beautiful tawny hair like Sara's!'

'That would be a shame. Black hair shines like a bird's wing!'

She couldn't stop the words torn from her. 'I know I have to look my best for Claudia's friends!'

'I don't know why you keep on about Claudia!' Ryan said mildly. 'Can't you ignore her?'

'As she ignores me?' Her winged brows shot up.

'When, exactly?' His tone hardened.

'When you're not there. Not that it matters. She doesn't really bother me, not for a long time, which seems an odd motivation for coming to her party!'

'Did you buy yourself anything?' he asked.

'I spent every precious cent. I hope you don't mind. I may even be a talking point, the dress is so plain!'

'The most dangerous kind, like that red thing you had on the other night. I've noticed you're not one for frills!'

'It seems the only way until I fill out considerably!' she said quite seriously.

'What you have will do nicely!' The glance he turned on her made her senses clamour whatever she wanted and she visibly composed herself before speaking again.

'Are there any other festivities planned?' she asked.

'A continuation of them as far as I know. I haven't had all that much time to remark them. I leave all that kind of thing to my mother.'

'You must have put considerable pressure on her to invite me,' she observed with some irony.

'I've the feeling we've been through this before!'

'She hates me!' Kylie said without emphasis or heat.

'I hope not!' His beautiful mouth thinned.

'You know she does, in a civilised way. I'm a little Nobody from Nowhere. It makes her angry to think I might come close to the throne.'

'Is that your intention? To do that you'd have to give yourself to me, and you'll never do that willingly!'

'I know what I want!' Kylie shook her head fiercely.

'And I think you're mad!'

'Maybe. What's mad anyway? We're all a little mad, with our burnt-out dreams.'

'I take it you're anticipating your next meeting with Rex?'

'Why do you expect the worst of him?' she asked, bitter-sweet. 'You're so arrogant, so sure of yourself. It's built in. Anyway, Rex always behaves beautifully. A typical landed gentleman!'

'Taking just what he wants!'

'Such a neat little triangle, isn't it? You and your two enemies!'

'And you can both plot away merrily. It makes no difference. No one can begin to take what's mine!'

'I think it would be good for you!'

He let out a groan of exasperation. 'Your *words* leave me in little doubt, but I see you more perfectly. You'll wound yourself far more than you'll ever wound me!'

'Let's see how things turn out, shall we?' she invited, her dark eyes sparkling. 'It was really something asking Sara out. It pleased her so much!'

'I fancy she thinks she's going to land herself a rich husband!'

'What's wrong with that?' she asked aggressively.

'Is that what you want, you strange little girl? A rich husband or anarchy. It's unhealthy for you to be so obsessed with your destructive thoughts!'

'Surely you're exaggerating?' She tilted her head back, exposing the lovely line of her throat.

'Am I?'

'Yes. You don't think I sit around thinking about you all day!'

'So we come to it!' he said tautly, turning his head and pinning her gaze.

Her poise simply deserted her. 'What is it you want? Love and respect? It's not possible!'

'I'd like something else than this incurable vendetta. You do nothing to help yourself!'

'You're absolutely right! Sacrifice is not in my mind!'

'It's just as well you're not reading mine!'

'Then suppose you tell me.'

'I wouldn't know where to begin!' he said in a dry voice. 'And it would take all day. Merrick wants to buy one of my colts.'

'Which one?' she asked, and her voice sounded anxious.

'Ebony Flash!' He glanced sidelong at her. 'He wants to race him.'

'Hang *him*! Why don't you?'

'I breed the horses, Kylie. I leave others to race them or whatever.'

'I say you could do that as well,' she said, in a

sharp, convinced tone. 'I'd love to see one of ours carry off the Melbourne Cup!'

'One already has. Stunning Boy!'

'I mean carrying our colours. You breed magnificent thoroughbreds and then let the new owners take all the rewards!'

'I think we've got enough to suffice!' he said, a millionaire many times over.

'But wouldn't you like to see the horse you bred carrying your colours to victory? You've bred such a lot of winners, why can't you hold on to the best and race them yourself?'

'Me?' He smiled and checked for a moment. 'Just how many hours are there in a day?'

'You'd like to, wouldn't you?' she persisted.

'Yes, I would. You share my love of horses, Kylie. You know how I feel, but a man can only do so much.'

'Then why don't you give Jeff more to do? Christy as well. Both of them take it pretty easy. They could work so much harder and not notice it. It's even understandable in a way. You're so—so——'

'Yes?'

'Super-efficient. It's even frightening how tough you are. Your brothers aren't in the least envious of you, to give them credit, but your initiative robs them of——'

'Please be candid!' he invited, a touch of sarcasm in his voice.

'I'm trying to be. The strong can make the weak incurably lazy. Your family lead too comfortable a life. You kill yourself, and you don't have to.'

'Oh, I have to all right!' he said dryly. 'However,

I'll have a small talk with them the minute I get home. I don't know how it will work out, but then I can always look to you for help. Tell me, what shall I do with the colt?'

Kylie gazed at his profile intently. 'Are you really asking me?'

'You heard the question. Besides, you love the colt.'

'Certainly I love him!' she said crossly. 'But it's none of my business!' Then because she thought her voice might sound laced with self-pity she said briskly, 'Why let Merrick have him?'

'We both know his ambition is to own a champion and he's a lavish spender!'

'I thought you were going to breed from him eventually?'

'It's necessary to sell most of my horses, Kylie. That's the business I'm in. If I wanted to I could have the biggest stud in the country, but I think I'm fully engaged!'

'And *I* say you should make your brothers work harder. Have a talk to them, lay it on the line. God knows, you're formidable enough with the rest of us. Delegate more duties and come into your own. You're entitled to a little relaxation. What could be better than horse-racing?'

He glanced at her with unaffected surprise, his sapphire blue eyes brilliant with mockery. 'Is this *Kylie*?'

'That's my name!' she said, subsiding.

'What a surprise! Can it really be you? You almost sounded on my side.'

'Oh well!' She shrugged her delicate shoulders in a distinctly Gallic fashion, for in truth she had forgotten her traumas to view him and the whole situation objectively. Often her father had come in at night quite angry about the boys not pulling their weight. They were allowed to enjoy life to the full and in their privileged position as Langtons the staff could hardly call them to order. It was Ryan who had to be everywhere to give the men their orders and see they were carried out, Ryan who had to take charge and responsibility in case of sickness and accident, and tribal feuds. He was the brilliant business man and even the showman who put on the big sales of the pastoral world, livening them up with polo matches and amateur race meetings and always a gala ball. Perhaps she was asking too much. Ryan knew his brothers well and what they were capable of, but Kylie was certain there was tremendous room for improvement.

In a way the boys' lack of dedication and inside information was an advantage, for Rex often tried to pick their brains, only to come up with nothing. Ryan was known for playing a very cool hand and close to his chest. He was the brains and driving force behind a very successful and famous station, and apparently he trusted no one outside himself. The fact that Kylie wanted him to race his own horses came as a surprise even to her. She hadn't even thought of it consciously until he mentioned selling Ebony Flash to Colonel Merrick. She couldn't understand herself or why she had supported his cause. It was like a momentary aberration when she found herself on the wrong side, a circumstance that so inflamed her that she fell into a near-silence until they were coming in over Narghilla Downs. Much as she disliked the thought of descending she was almost relieved. Ryan appeared to have enjoyed her inconsistency and the evident withdrawal.

Her stomach muscles knotted as she braced herself for the shock of the wheels touching the runway. They touched, bounced once and settled perfectly, the twin propellers sending out sprays of dust and dry grass until the plane came to a stop and the motors were cut.

Through the window Kylie could see Laura and her father waving a greeting. They were standing against a Range Rover and their smiles didn't waver even when they saw Ryan had brought her along for the ride. He went ahead and opened out the cabin door, then waited for Kylie. She felt a little shaky, and she certainly looked very fragile in her classic slacks and silk shirt.

Almost impatiently he reached up for her, tightening his hands around her slender waist, then swinging her to the ground where he kept his hands on her for a moment as though she was bound to fall over. A surge of childish resentment went through her, but she managed to follow him at a few respectful paces, conscious that this wasn't her world and Mrs Merrick would be sure to rub that in.

Laura wore her adoring smile, and Kylie felt infinitely sorry for her. Laura was an heiress with a difference, very self-effacing. She was always expensively dressed, but without flair or an eye to colour, and her long well bred face was just short of plain. Her one big asset outside her father's money was undoubtedly her smile. It was full of good health and good humour and her teeth were really beautiful. It even managed to include Kylie.

The Colonel, hardly a handsome man, thought his

daughter beautiful, so her freckled skin and her sandy colouring didn't distress him. Laura had been in love with Ryan Langton for most of her life and the thought of a marriage between them filled him with satisfaction and longing.

He looked now at Ryan's ward and thought yet again that she reminded him of an ivory carving with a still, inscrutable expression. Beside Ryan's splendid rangy figure she looked a mere figurine. Hers was an unusual beauty. One would either admire it enormously or find it too exotic. Her hair was a rare, true black with a marvellous sheen, her face modelled with extreme delicacy, the brilliant dark eyes almost too big for it. She was a chic little thing too, quite unconventional, but penniless, of course. She wasn't the catch Laura was, who at five feet eight in her stockinged feet seemed to tower over the girl. Nevertheless he greeted her with extreme courtesy and some warmth, and Kylie had to admit that both Laura and her father were basically very kind people. Mrs Merrick was a superb snob whose ambitions for her only child were enormous. Kylie expected to encounter that lacklustre stare shortly. Mrs Merrick had never liked her, for there had been something wrong in her entry into their exclusive circle.

Ryan said something to her and she didn't answer, hardly hearing. If he'd come to clinch a deal why didn't he do it? she thought with intensity. She was feeling weary and her silk shirt clung to her back. On the trip up to the homestead she took no part in the conversation. It was all about horses, which in itself should have interested her greatly, but she didn't want to see Ebony Flash race under the Merrick colours.

She'd been there the night he had been born, a beautiful high-bred little creature with wobbly too-long legs and a gleaming metallic black coat. She knew it was crazy, but she had come to love him as her very own. The Colonel was speaking confidently as though anything he wanted would be his own and he was known to have paid some spectacular prices for high-class thoroughbreds. The Annual Thoroughbred Sale on Sovereign River was a couple of months off and Kylie had always known Ebony Flash would be included among the fifteen or so yearlings. His sire, Ebony King, was one of their prize stallions.

From the high seat of the Rover with its superb road view, Kylie could look out over the property and not be noticed. It was in splendid condition, the vision beautiful. The seasons had been unexpectedly kind. In a territory notoriously drought-stricken with all its catastrophic repercussions, the rivers, the creeks and the great maze of waterways and channels were brimming with the flood waters brought down from the deluged Far North. The continent's cattle kings in their south-west stronghold thanked God for this miraculous season with the desert, incomparably beautiful, thickly cushioned in wildflowers as far as the horizon, the white and gold glory of the paper daisies, the poppies and the green pussy tails, the blood-red desert peas, the purple Morgan flowers and the spider lilies, the annual saltbush and firebush, the countless varieties of wildflowers that cloaked the red sand and turned the blinding gibber plains into endless, fragrant desert gardens that hid the graves of the pioneers and explorers. This wasn't Sovereign River with the desert for its border, but it still made Kylie's heart beat with pleasure. She loved the land no matter how savage it became, for she was a true Nature's child.

Station horses grazed in the paddocks and she could see the fat cattle fanned out over the hills and drinking at the tree-lined creek. The homestead was still hidden in its oasis of trees. The Colonel was a breeder of first-rate stud stock and although his family had not pioneered the property or built the picturesque home-stead he was preserving the spirit of the place and greatly enhancing the prosperity of the South-West. He was a good station master too, for he had just the right combination of qualities to handle the coloured people on his vast property as well as his staff. No matter what their troubles the natives always came to him to settle them and find justice, and he was strong enough to persuade them against their own judgment.

Brilliantly coloured lorikeets scattered and screeched as they swept up the four-mile drive from the entrance gates, and soon they had their first view of the house. It stood above the lagoons of Narghilla creek, a comfortable, pleasantly unpretentious build-ing, very solidly built. The beautiful gardens surround-ing it greatly added to its charm and there was no shortage of labour to keep the rolling green lawns, the magnificent native trees, the introduced exotic shrubs and the great curving flower beds tended. Two col-oured house boys were busy in the grounds and they looked up to smile and wave as the Range Rover swept past, their glistening black eyes bright with health and a natural racial merriment.

Mrs Merrick was waiting for them in the shade of the deep covered veranda, an attractive smile on her face that faded abruptly as Kylie stepped out into the sunlight. Evidently I haven't been planned on! Kylie thought, well used to being made uncomfortable by this woman.

Dinah Merrick came forward to meet them, her hand outstretched. 'Ryan, how lovely to see you! Kylie, how are you, my dear?' The thin lips smiled, but there was a rigid stare in the eyes. 'Do come in, won't you? I've had afternoon tea prepared. You were right on time, Ryan, as usual. Tell me, how's the family? Busy with plans for Claudia's party, I shouldn't wonder. It will be the event of the season!'

She led the way into the spacious hallway with Ryan responding to all of her questions with what seemed to Kylie impersonal charm for the most part. He was a very confident man and she suspected Mrs Merrick meant absolutely nothing to him, if not all women. Looking at her vivid profile, Kylie realised she was only in her mid-forties and still considered herself very attractive. Unlike her husband and daughter, Dinah had decided good looks, and speaking to Ryan she seemed a different woman, her tall, lean figure shown to advantage in close-fitting pants and a blue and bronze striped body shirt. She even managed to make her daughter look mousy, and she was a good twenty years younger than her husband. One of her problems was that she had never loved him and she was deeply disappointed in her daughter. She could never understand why Laura had to take after her father. After all, dark colouring was said to predominate and Laura had inherited Bryan's nondescript colouring exactly. She had even refused having her sandy locks professionally tinted to a more becoming shade and she was desperately in love with the wrong man.

Ambitious as she was for her daughter, Dinah could still see that Ryan Langton was a very masculine and exciting man with his sensuous mouth and his brilliant blue eyes. To her astonishment she had even dreamt about him a few times and afterwards wished violently for her own vibrant youth. She might have interested Ryan, but she was having the devil's own job thrusting Laura upon him. If a marriage could be arranged she would go delirious with joy that might easily turn to jealousy. She longed to thrust Kylie out of the house—there was something about that little upstart she disliked, something that hinted at ecstatic, wild passions for all that remote little air. It had been a fortunate day for the girl when her father had been killed, Dinah considered. How else could she have entered their world? Ryan took the dead man's request too seriously. After all, he had only been a leading hand.

Kylie sitting opposite, sipping her tea, was well aware of Dinah Merrick's churning thoughts. She even braced herself when the men went out to the stables and she was left alone with the Merrick women. Laura asked her kindly how she was liking teaching while Dinah waited impatiently for her daughter to dispense with such trivialities.

'How long are you staying with us this time?' she just barely interrupted, not in the least interested in Kylie's career.

'For Claudia's party!'

'I gather she asked you?'

Laura looked pained, but Kylie answered Dinah's question evenly enough:

'*Ryan* asked me.'

'He takes his role of guardian very seriously.'

'He takes all his roles very seriously, Mother. Naturally Kylie would be invited. It would be quite unthinkable to leave her out!'

'I wasn't suggesting any such thing, my darling!' Dinah smiled tightly. 'I only meant it's common knowledge that Claudia and Kylie don't see eye to eye on anything. It goes back some years, I believe?'

'Assuredly nothing in it, Mrs Merrick!' Kylie smiled with her mouth only. 'In any case, Claudia does what she's told, as you well know!'

'Mother, this is rather an unhappy subject—let's change it!' Laura said helpfully. 'I suppose you've bought a beautiful dress with you, Kylie. You have such perfect taste!'

'It's rather plain!'

'Wht colour?' Dinah asked sharply. 'Mine's a bitter chocolate chiffon and Laura's is blue organza.'

'Laura should never wear blue!' Kylie replied instantly. 'Nor organza. She wants something with a graceful flow of skirt—perhaps a jersey in a sage green to pick up her eyes, and she wants her hair arranged in a chignon with maybe a large, beautiful rose pinned at the back.'

'I picked Laura's dress myself!' Dinah said in a steely voice.

'Then I'm surprised. You have excellent taste!'

'I don't absolutely *have* to wear it!' Laura exclaimed, momentarily seeing herself so much more feminine and alluring. 'My eyes *do* have green flecks in them.'

'They're decidedly green!' Kylie said emphatically. 'If I were you, Laura, I'd fly down to Adelaide and find myself just the dress to match them. You still have time.'

'My dear, you may have no one, but my daughter has me,' snapped Dinah. 'The blue dress is extremely appropriate and it cost the earth!'

'I shouldn't think that would matter if it doesn't suit!' Kylie turned her head coolly. 'If you like, Laura, I'll come with you on a shopping spree. I know your *father* would love to see you looking your best!' There was the very slightest emphaisis on the word and Dinah's cheeks ran the red flag.

'Each time I see you your hostility becomes more pronounced!' she said angrily.

'Aren't you being overly dramatic, Mrs Merrick? I have no feelings about you one way or the other. Laura I would like to help. It seems to me she could look charming with a little help!'

'I have *complete* charge of my daughter's wardrobe!' Dinah pointed out, her tone ugly.

'Then Laura should do something for herself. After all, you're—what? Twenty-five, Laura?'

'Twenty-six in June!' Laura burst out like a child. 'Don't be angry, Mother. I'm sure Kylie has the kindest motives for speaking out. Now that she mentions it I do think green would be a better colour. The blue seems to drain all the colour from my face and it makes my eyes fade away into my face.'

'I won't let you buy anything now. I think we've spent quite enough!'

'Then I'll take the blue back. We must be among their very best customers, I'm sure there won't be any problem there. You did say you'd come with me, Kylie? I'm hopeless when it comes to clothes. That's why Mother has to go to so much trouble. She's really very disappointed in me, aren't you, Mother?'

'You mustn't think that, my dear!' Dinah said grimly. 'This is *my* home, Kylie, yet you seem to be endeavouring to take my place.'

'What, in suggesting a different dress for Laura?'

'In persuading her you know better than I do!'

'That's ridiculous!' Kylie gave a little false tinkle of laughter. 'We're just being girls together. I'm sure you'll be delighted with our choice. Seeing we're going to have a little time together we might pick out a few other things as well. I know the Colonel would deny Laura nothing to make her happy.'

Dinah was wrenched by an anger so violent it showed in her face and the sudden clenching of her hands. 'I've often wondered why Elizabeth dislikes you so much. She's told me herself!'

Laura gave a strangled gasp. 'That's not true! Mrs Langton has never said one word about Kylie!'

'Perhaps not to *you*, dear! You're so very naïve!'

'No!' Laura murmured, distressed, her freckles standing out on her whitened face. 'Mrs Langton is a very elegant lady. She doesn't make personal remarks!'

'And of course *I* do!' her mother said bitterly. 'You see now, Kylie, why I don't welcome you into my home. You're a trouble-maker, you disturb everything you touch. You carry an atmosphere with you. You're such a cold little thing. You've upset me and you've upset my daughter. You would even try to turn her against me!'

Kylie stood up, not in the least shattered, aware of Dinah Merrick as her husband and daughter never would be. 'Would that be so terrible?' she asked ironically. 'Excuse me now, won't you. Thank you for the tea. It was very refreshing. Laura, would you like to join me outside? The grounds are beautiful. I've never seen them looking so well!'

Laura shot up awkwardly and knocked against the table. She looked anxiously at her mother for approval, but Dinah, with tightened lips, was catching at a precious cup jiggling in its saucer. Laura sighed and turned to join Kylie who was watching her with interest and faint sympathy in her dark eyes. She felt guilty and miserable, helpless to change anything. Almost too late she was realising that though her mother was always impeccably turned out she was woefully unsuccessful at making her daughter look good. It just couldn't be deliberate. The blue dress with its matching jacket had been the most expensive one in the range. It would look fabulous on someone like Camilla Russell, a golden blonde with blue eyes and a deliciously rounded body, but Kylie was quite right—it did nothing for her. In fact it would have suited almost anyone before her.

They walked out into the garden and Laura expressed her apology. 'I'm sorry about that. I don't know what came over Mother. You really do rub one another up the wrong way—some kind of chemical reaction, I guess. I've always liked you, Kylie. I admire you too. You've lots of courage and you're doing well for yourself. I understand it's quite difficult to get a post at St Margaret's. You must have ability and it can't have been easy for you, orphaned so early in life. Ryan is really wonderful, isn't he? I suppose you can't thank him enough!'

It wasn't necessary to answer, for the men were coming back along the gravel path that led from the stables to the house. 'Every time I see him I'm struck by the look of him!' Laura said sentimentally. 'I'd love to look my best for the party. Did you mean what you said about coming to Adelaide with me? We could go to Sydney if you liked—or Melbourne.'

'Where did you get the blue?' asked Kylie.

'Roberta's.'

'Then Adelaide will do. I'm sure she'll find something just right for you. She's an artist in her own way. How come she let you even try on blue chiffon?'

'Oh, she's devoted to Mother, and Mother liked the blue.'

'Mm!' Kylie murmured, and frowned at the ground. Dinah Merrick was too clever with her own dressing to exhibit such poor taste for her daughter. Her dark eyes flickered upwards, catching Laura's radiant smile, her heart in her eyes.

'How goes it?' Ryan asked, and came up to them.

Laura's breath seemed to catch in her throat. 'I wonder if I might borrow Kylie, the day after tomorrow?'

'Oh, what for?'

The Colonel's hazel eyes looked from one to the other. 'Something she has her heart set on, by the look of her!'

'Oh, nothing very mysterious!' said Laura. 'Kylie has some ideas for my party dress!'

'Where's your mother?' the Colonel asked.

'In the house, of course. I know I've got one already, but Kylie suggested quite another colour. If I'm boring you, Ryan, I'll stop!'

'No, I'm fascinated!' he replied, his brilliant eyes finding and holding Kylie's as though he suspected she had been up to some mischief.

'Laura's decided to return the one she's got for another,' she explained. 'It's a kind of experiment and I think it will come off.'

'What has your mother to say?' Colonel Merrick asked his daughter fondly. 'I know she spent the best part of two thousand dollars!'

'Mother doesn't mind!' Laura said with disconcerting untruthfulness, giving Ryan all her attention. 'I'm determined to look my best!'

'I say!' the Colonel laughed, and pressed her shoulder. 'Spend what you like, my dear. There'll be a large crowd with all the women vying to look the most attractive. The event of the season, I'll be bound!'

'That's nothing if Ryan decides to marry!' Laura announced, then immediately blushed.

'How lovely!' Kylie murmured maliciously. 'It's nice to have that thrill in store!'

'Don't expect it this year!' Ryan answered dryly. 'I was just telling the Colonel I intend to race Ebony Flash.'

'It's true!' the Colonel said, looking at his daughter. 'I'm disappointed. Then again, I'm not. I've always felt Ryan could race his own horses and he's promised me one of Storm Cloud's. He's a full brother of Ebony King.'

'When did you think of it, Ryan?' Laura looked at him solemnly.

'Actually Kylie brought up the subject. I think she sees herself in the winners' circle at Flemington!'

'Apparently it wasn't a fantasy!' She managed to meet his eyes.

'You're good at advising people!' Ryan turned to Laura, who was studying him with a faintly mournful expression. 'I'll take you both in to Adelaide if you like.'

She didn't even have to consider. Her face altered magically. 'How marvellous! How can you spare the time?'

'I've had some of the family jewellery re-set for Claudia—necklace and earrings. There's a matching bracelet, but she can wait until she gets married for that. Naturally it's a big secret, and there's the business of picking it up!'

'Oh, I *see*,' Laura smiled, her eyes crinkling. 'She'll be thrilled, take my word for it. What are the stones?'

'It's a set of diamond and aquamarine pieces that belonged to my great-grandmother.'

'I'd like to see the woman who wouldn't be interested in that!' the Colonel smiled, and pulled out his pipe, going through the business of filling and lighting it. "Best pipe I've ever had!' he said confidentially. 'Tell your mother, darling, Ryan must be going. She'll want to say goodbye.'

Laura nodded and walked off briskly towards the house. Her mother, who had been looking through the drawing room curtains, met her as she walked into the house. 'Ryan's leaving!' said Laura, blinking in the sudden gloom.

'There's something pathetic about you!' her mother said curtly. 'I'll never manage to marry you off. Why can't you make an effort?'

'That's the whole point, Mother. One shouldn't *have* to!'

'I suppose every girl gets a husband without trying!' Dinah said acidly.

'Ryan's magnificent! He'd never look at me and I could never hold the position of mistress of Sovereign River!'

'Why not? Because you haven't the strength or the purpose. Men don't always marry the women they desire. There are other considerations—I should have thought you'd realise that. Are you going to leave him open to that little bitch?'

Laura started back and looked at her mother in a startled way. 'I can't think who you mean!'

'Then I'll spell it out for you. K-Y-L-I-E. Kylie!'

Laura considered this seriously. 'No!' she said at last. 'There's something between them, but it isn't love. One can always tell. Ryan has given her every chance she's had and there's nothing to prevent her loving him, but she doesn't. It's suddenly occurred to me that she doesn't act especially grateful.'

'It's all quite simple!' Dinah ground out, and swept past her daughter. 'When it's all said and done, hate comes very close to love. Accept that he plays an important part in her life—the most important part, I'd say. She's a woman, isn't she, and she's very clever. Ryan's had women falling all over him for most of his life. He just may be struck by her peculiar designing ways. You're a useless thing beside her!'

'Then she doesn't make me *feel* it!' Laura replied quietly and with dignity. 'But you, Mother, are something else again!'

CHAPTER FIVE

THEY took off in a brisk cross wind, Kylie gazing rather apprehensively out over the shimmering airstrip. It was a way of life in the Outback riding the vast distances in private light planes, but she could never feel enthusiastic, or ever confident enough to take out a licence as Ryan had several times suggested. Claudia held a licence, as did the boys, without Ryan's rating or impressive logged hours of flying time; nevertheless they made it look easy, and it might have been, Kylie considered, if one didn't have to contend with thermals that made it seem such a matter of life and death to her. The familiar staggering, the fall and quick rise made her long for a more rugged structure than the sophisticated Beechcraft, but Ryan might have been riding his horse from the easy, confident look of him, not the buffeting air currents, as he cruised serenely now to up and above the clouds.

The butterflies in her stomach stopped their clammy beating and in a few minutes she had herself under control. Many people feared flying, and there had been a tragic incident on the station eighteen months before when a single-engined Bonanza on route from Adelaide to Alice had come down in the hill country, killing the pilot and his two passengers. The Aviation people had stayed on the property to determine the cause of the accident, and she remembered it as vividly as if it had been a week ago.

'Nervy little thing, aren't you?'

'Only at certain times!' She shrugged it aside. 'Anyone who lives with planes knows that accidents are on all the time!'

'I thought you didn't care either way!'

'What's that supposed to mean?' she demanded.

'You should be *living*, Kylie, not following me round with that look in your eyes!'

'It's not adoration!'

'I know that!' Ryan said with his usual dry precision. 'You'd deny it to me with your dying breath!'

'You get enough of it anyway. You'll just have to adjust to my curious attitude.'

'I thought I had!' He smiled at her sidelong. 'Kylie, of the calculating eyes!'

'It might pay you to take my little phobias seriously,' she said bitterly.

'On the contrary, I'm going to help you get rid of them.'

'You haven't had much success so far.'

'Oh, I thought I'd give you a little time.'

'A friend indeed!'

'You only say that because you don't like me. You may change your mind.'

'That's unlikely to happen!' she said rapidly. 'You can't recognise a good woman when you see one. Poor Laura is hopelessly in love with you.'

He shrugged. 'I don't pretend to be unaware of it.'

'Dinah as well!'

'Why, that's not allowed!' he said, and frowned.

'It's masterly, the way you ignore her so charmingly. Very sardonic!'

'I generally try to squash crushes!' he murmured absently.

'The really great thing about Dinah is how unkind she is to her daughter,' said Kylie.

'What's on your brilliant little mind?' His tone hardened. 'I hope you're not about to make trouble. You thrive on it!'

'Haven't you noticed how Laura dresses?' she asked.

'God forgive me, I've never really noticed Laura!'

'You *would*!' she insisted, 'if she just made the effort to distinguish her self. The Colonel has great presence, yet he's a very plain man. Laura should follow up her assets. She has an open, well-bred face and beautiful teeth.'

'Laura's all right!' he murmured lazily, rather amused.

'No matter. I'm going to take her to Adelaide and you won't know her by the time I'm finished with her. I like making people over.'

'So I've noticed. Why don't you have a go on yourself?'

'There's nothing wrong with me!'

'Ah!' he jeered.

'There is *not*!'

'I realise what you *look* like. I'm merely considering your behavioural patterns. What I don't understand is how you got her away from her mother.'

'There's spirit in Laura!' Kylie said firmly. 'It's got to come out. Besides, she's got nothing to lose. Mrs

Merrick mightn't be fully aware of it, but she definitely doesn't want a daughter more dashing than she
is. The inevitable must come. I'm going to take Laura
in hand.'

'Not for *my* sake, I hope!'

'For her *own* sake!' she exploded violently. 'I like
Laura. For a very rich girl she can see there are other
creatures on God's earth.'

'So it's personal. Another one of your hang-ups?
You've been spoilt rotten yourself the last five years!'

'I have *not*!' she said tightly, controlling her anger.

'It will strike you eventually. I've been bending over
backwards to keep you happy.'

'I have to know why?' she asked with extreme
sarcasm.

'Maybe I feel sorry for you.'

'Don't ever do that!'

'Every picture tells a story!' retorted Ryan. 'You
should see yourself. You're so rigid I could break your
neck now with the slightest blow!'

'It's reasonable to suppose you might feel like it
occasionally.'

'Possibly, though you're admirably designed for
making love to.'

It fell off his tongue so deftly it took a few seconds
for the first impact to hit her. She was actually
shocked as though her mind had never contemplated
such a possibility.

'That appears to have floored you!' he observed.

'I find it offensive!'

'We can soon find out. I know you think you're my
superior. Let's see if you're my equal!'

'I had no idea you had such a romantic turn of mind.'

'Who said anything about romantic? I'm talking about teaching you a lesson!'

'You'd dearly love to, wouldn't you?'

'Yes, somewhere in the desert. I could put down now. Then we'd see how desperate you are to stay alive!' He moved the controls and the plane slid down through the sky.

'You don't frighten me!' Kylie tried to hide her panic.

'How do you know until I push you to the limit?'

'Crash this plane and you're in big trouble!'

'You know better than that, Kylie, I'm just waiting for you to yell for help. I'd really like that to have you sobbing and helpless. I see no reason why you should always be the one handing out punishment.'

She was breathing deeply and her hands were clenched on the seat, the harness cutting into her. 'I hate you. Oh, I hate you!'

'What's the panic?' Ryan pulled the stick back and the plane started to climb again.

'I'll never come with you again.'

'Oh yes, you will. I'm not going to waste any more time treating you so carefully. You're a woman now and you're due for your first brush with violence!'

She threw back her head, more colour in her face now. 'Why, I've been used to violence all my life. You set the pattern. Sovereign River.'

'Why do you bracket us together?'

'You're no different in my mind—the man and the land!'

'Then you can expect the unpredictable, can't you?'

'All except being made love to!'

He glanced at her and she turned away with involuntary haste, plunged into a seething whirlpool of hate. He looked very hard and experienced, with a ruthless purpose his cousin Rex could never realise. They had been airborne for half an hour and Kylie felt vaguely ill, overwrought and excited. What devil had possessed him to frighten her like that, each of them trying to bring the other down for different reasons? She arched her aching body and went to unfasten the seat harness.

'Don't do that!' he rebuked her.

'Why not?' With his brilliant blue eyes on her she snapped the clasp shut again.

'Because you're safer that way.'

'I don't follow you!' she said with tight fury. 'One minute you're trying to kill me, the next you're terribly anxious!'

'Please, Kylie, you get no marks for exaggeration. You'll be in far more dangerous places!'

'I wish I'd never come,' she sighed.

'Why did you?'

'You *claimed* you wanted me there!'

He put out a hand and turned her face to him. 'So I do!' She tried to shrug her head aside, but his fingers tightened painfully under her delicate jaw. 'Tell me about it, Kylie. Why are you so certain you hate me?'

'It goes back a million years.' The fingers tightened still more and her eyes filled with tears. 'You have no claim on me. Take your hand off my face!'

'Say *please*!'

It was the strangest thing to be looking so deeply

into his jewelled, Judas eyes. A tear spilled on to his hand and he gave a sharp exclamation. 'You little fool!'

'Why, because you can't make me do what I don't want?'

'Forgive me, Kylie, but I could make you do anything I like. You're here with me now, aren't you?'

She drew in her breath sharply and put both hands to her face, smoothing the jawline, pleased to endure the faint pain. 'You're really a violent man, aren't you?'

'I know that you deserve what you get.'

'Are you sure you're not in some kind of danger yourself?' Her dark eyes were enormous with a flame at the centre.

'Good luck to you, Kylie, whatever you intend. The boys are sitting ducks, but it's worth remembering what I told you. Leave Rex alone.'

'You don't think he'd marry me?'

'I think he'd take you and break you!'

She passed her hand shakily over her face. 'Thank you for the warning.'

'I'd kill him if he did.'

'What a hopeless mixture you are!' Something about his eyes and the set of his mouth frightened her.

'Do you think so? I mean it. If you want to bring violence down on your head give Rex some unnecessary encouragement. You'll pay for it!'

'I don't expect I mean the least little thing to him.'

'He wants you. Pretty savagely, I'd say.'

'Good!' she retorted.

'You reckless little fool! He might want you, but he certainly won't marry you. I repeat, Rex does what he's told. He can fool around all he likes, but when he marries his bride will have a lot more to fall back on then her beauty and brains. Not that you use yours.'

Caution and the characteristic arrogant tone of his voice made Kylie subside. She could see those lean brown hands turn to fists, the wide shoulders and the rippling muscles of his back and torso. She could appreciate that if driven he would rip into his cousin just as he planned. It might be just the piece of good luck she was looking for. An elusive feeling was tearing at her, but she couldn't think what it was. Instinct told her to goad him no longer, but she was on fire with her own involved emotions and increasingly careless of disturbing the devil in him.

'I hope he likes my dress!' she found herself murmuring. 'Let me think, I've never worn opal colours before. Do I dare ask for the stone my father left me? I was always told it was very valuable.'

'We might have a totally different idea of *valuable*, Kylie.'

'Mmmmm! I don't have your enormous reserves to draw on. Give me a figure?'

'I've had the opal valued at two thousand dollars.'

'That's a lot of money, isn't it?' she commented.

'If you say so. The depth of colour is excellent. I've had it cut and polished. You can wear it now if you like.'

'It might bring me luck.'

'Some people find them unlucky!' he pointed out.

'Well, I don't. I think they're glorious. My father brought that back from Lightning Ridge. He had it stowed away for years—my insurance, he used to call it. Are you sure you got the best price?'

'I'm not even going to answer that. You're a frightful little brat.'

'I learned in a good school,' she retorted.

'So you need to get your own back?'

'I'd like to explore a few ways.'

'You'll get your chance. We're over Sovereign River now.'

'A thousand miles from nowhere! Home of the cattle kings!'

'You love it, Kylie. Why be ashamed of exposing your heart?'

'That desolate landscape?' she said bravely.

'You belong there just as surely as the black swan. There are millions of them down there, the greatest mass of wildfowl I've ever seen. Every curving channel of the River, every waterhole and lagoon is invaded with birds, countless thousands of them flocking in to breed. The lignum swamps can hardly support the colonies of ibis. Even the pelicans that breed in the remote swamps are a common sight. It's a season of plenty. We're all drunk on it. The corellas are turning the coolibahs white and the budgerigars never stop chattering from dawn to dark. Desolate?' he said, and his blue eyes were brooding, 'the Wild Heart has come alive. The flowering annuals are all out, the shrubs and succulents, winding away to the far horizon. A man couldn't ride over them in a week. The most inhospitable regions are covered in the wild hibiscus and the morning glories. It would be difficult to imagine a more beautiful landscape at the moment.'

'I'm going to take a long ride!' Kylie decided.

'And you'll be rewarded. All the colour in the world is down there.'

'It's also true that nothing could mean more to you!'

He was silent quite a time. 'I know I couldn't go on without it,' he agreed.

'That's the same as saying the land is the most important thing in the world to you.'

'Don't you understand that?'

'Yes, I do.'

'Then you're a rare woman. I always thought you would be.'

'There's a great magic about it,' Kylie admitted.

'So you're trapped.'

'We're not talking about me.'

'Oh, I thought we were!'

'I seek nothing that is yours,' she assured him.

'You only want to hurt me.' The lightning blue of his eyes took her breath away. She was profoundly disturbed, far from indifferent to him.

'Don't worry about it until the time comes!' she offered.

'Maybe you're the one who should worry,' said Ryan. 'You brought yourself to my attention long ago.'

'Don't think I owe *you* my life!' she said with rising passion.

'Or gratitude. I've not heard a word of that.'

'I've worked hard to repay your interest.'

'Don't sound so virtuous. It doesn't become you. You're no angel, Kylie!'

'Surely you don't expect perfection in a ward?'

'I didn't expect a dark enchantress either, but that's what I got.'

She frowned uncomprehendingly at his reply, not realising or even understanding the qualities in herself that made men reach out for her and women as jealous as bats out of hell.

'You make it sound as if I've had dozens of love affairs,' she said.

'You've inspired a few fantasies, I'll bet!'

'You flatter me!'

'You certainly don't flatter yourself. In fact, you're quite unconscious of your own appeal. It's one of the odd things I like about you.'

'What other things?' she challenged.

'Oh, you're very spirited and resourceful. An explosive little thing, really. I can't help being drawn to you despite myself.'

There was something in his voice, a depth and a nuance she didn't wish to interpret or acknowledge, though the voice alone gave her pleasure. It was a good voice with a very attractive, cutting timbre, a range and vitality one observed in trained actors and singers. Ryan was a very disruptive person altogether. She could barely tolerate sitting there beside him with the sunlight gilding the hard cleanness of his profile. She was about to withdraw again, but he wouldn't let her.

'Take it easy with Laura, won't you? No need to make her look too fabulous!'

'Right now, I can't think of a more exciting shopping experience. Her mother has been hassling her style for too long. You'll probably fall in love with her. You're both free to marry. It might even last. She'll bring quite a dowry with her, and that's what counts!'

'It's not strictly necessary, Kylie. I could learn to love a poor girl. You're the one who's making all the assumptions.'

'Then things must have changed with your mother. I mean, what woman could measure up?'

His glance swept her face and it wasn't gentle or kind. 'Are you deliberately trying to irritate me?' he demanded.

'I tend to, yes. Don't feel you have to grin and bear it. You keep too tight a rein on yourself, Ryan.'

'Maybe you're right. The point is if you're going to provoke me don't get angry if I retaliate.'

'Let's speak about it when we're on the ground. I try my best to like it, but I regard flying as a matter of life and death.'

'Strange, it relaxes me!'

'Oh well, you identify completely with whatever you're doing. I find it nerve-racking—that's why I want to talk about honest, all-important things, like landing the right wife for you. I don't exaggerate when I say it would be a tremendous task, and naturally your mother is entitled to her opinions.'

'I don't know if she's all that enthusiastic about Laura!' he pointed out dryly.

'I can take care of Laura, then she can take care of herself. You won't know her away from her rotten mother!'

'Don't start anything, Kylie!' he warned. 'I don't think you know it, but you're a catalyst.'

'I like a nice break in the routine. Tell me, how's dear Claudia? When did she finally relent and say I could come to her party?'

'You don't give yourself much of a breathing space,

do you?' he said. 'I suppose it's your emotional insecurity.'

'I suppose so. Tell me, who's covering the party? You Langtons make brilliant material. Your life style seems to compensate for other people's lack of it. When you find yourself a mate will *Women's Weekly* cover that?'

'Unlikely, Kylie!' he said bluntly. 'I dislike publicity. And women.'

'They're very susceptible to you. You're the answer to many a girl's dream. It should make you feel grateful. Of course, you're a lot older than I am, so I merely find you depressingly arrogant!'

'Oh?' his white smile was mocking. 'Everyone knows you're an odd kid.'

'The result of a few major traumas,' she said heatedly.

'And I for one am growing tired of them. You might find my behaviour a bit different from now on.'

'Oh, how?' she said sweetly. 'Is it possible you're going to show me a little compassion?'

'I don't think I'd get much of a kick out of that!'

'No, it wouldn't come easily to you.'

'Do you ever think before you speak?' he asked.

'I'm serious!' she maintained, shrugging her slim shoulders.

'Then you must know so am I!'

They were losing altitude and it seemed a nice, psychological trick on his part, for she sat up very straight, thrusting her head sideways to look out the window and over the wing. For no apparent reason her heart started hammering.

'Are we over Sovereign River?' she asked.

'Right!'

'We're losing altitude very quickly, aren't we?'

'What are we supposed to do?'

She turned to watch him carefully. 'God knows I wouldn't like to finish on the edge of a claypan.'

'It's the year of the Green Centre, didn't I tell you?'

'Have you decided to show me the property from the air?'

'I can't decide if the landing gear is stuck or not!'

'You're joking!' She clasped her hands sharply together.

'Do I look as if I am?' he asked crisply.

'Which is it? Show me.'

He pushed her hand away. 'Pray don't touch the controls. Then we'd really be in trouble.'

'You've got a radio.'

'I'm just trying to think where would be the best place to come down.'

Kylie passed a hand shakily through her curls. 'Couldn't you be mistaken? Try again.'

He flicked at the instrument panel, which to Kylie's eyes looked very elaborate, but nothing happened. 'Well, anyway, I think I can bring it down without wheels.'

'That's likely!' She looked down at the shimmering earth and visibly swallowed. 'They could search for us for ever and never find us.'

'What a stupefying thought! You and I alone in the desert.'

Her nervous hostility fairly flew for him. 'Tell me,

Ryan, is this a put-up job?' she demanded. 'Are you trying to frighten me?'

'Succeeding, I'd say! Everything is going to be all right. I don't know exactly what the problem is, but I'm some sort of a pilot, you know.'

'You're a good one!' she said heatedly.

'Why, thank you!' he drawled.

'I'm not even going to look.'

'Then I'll just have to find a big fat claypan all by myself. Any likely landing place will do—a dry creek bed if I can find one. Most of them are running a banker.'

'Use your radio!' she said, her dark eyes enormous in her ivory face.

'We're not in any trouble—yet!'

They were flying deeper now into the property, boring right into the heart of Sovereign River. The giant landscape looked amazingly green, with the silver, iridescent streak of the River snaking through the plains sending out tributaries of water channels and creeks. The whole country had blazed into life, transformed by the miraculous life-giving water. The hot dry hill country was thickly sown with paper daisies, the distant lagoons and swamps thrusting with waterlilies, pink and white, and the incomparable blue lotus.

The long minutes wore on and tension pervaded the air. They had slowed and lowered flaps and for a moment the aircraft tipped over on one wing. There was a lagoon beneath them alive with whistling ducks, magpie geese and the dancing brolgas. Thousands of birds congregated on and around the lagoons, the snowy white Royal spoonbills, the swans, and the blue cranes. A great flock rose in spectacular formation, but Kylie was feeling a little too hysterical to appreciate the sight. The melaleucas, the eucalyptus and the grevilleas were all out in flower, yellow, green and cream and brilliant orange splashes. The honey-eaters and parrots loved the blossoms. The aerial view was fantastic, the blazing desert gardens, the wildflowers that covered the hilly slopes and thickly cushioned the sand dunes, all the flowering trees standing out as bright patches of colour in the dark green.

A hot wind of trouble caught hold of the plane, but Ryan seemed prepared for it, coming down lower so they were almost over the trees. The homestead was in front of them slightly to the south-west. The outstation swept up, then the satellite buildings, the bungalows and office buildings, the station store and the great silver-roofed shed where the sales were held. Kylie was too agitated to speak and Ryan didn't seem inclined to speak to her. He had to bring them down safely—that was his job. She wanted to scream and even brought her hand up against her mouth. The landing strip was coming up at an alarming pace, an impressive, all-weather runway. Her hands fluttered and for a moment she thought she was going to be sick, then resoundingly the landing gear came down.

She gave a funny little gasp and turned her great eyes on him, vastly angry through the swift sense of reprieve.

'Any questions?' he asked.

'There was no trouble at all, was there?'

'There, you make me sound heartless!'

'What a rotten stunt!' she said angrily.

'Write it off as experience. You don't have the exclusive rights to enjoying yourself. Now sit still and be quiet. We're coming in to land.'

She braced herself, but they touched down as lightly as a dove on a windowsill, rolling in on the plane's fat wheels, cutting engines and gradually slowing to a halt. Now that they were safe, Kylie was surprised at the strength of her own anger. Her cheeks burned with colour, exaggering the jetty sparkle of her eyes. Ryan knew nothing about it, making an after-check, and she unclasped the seat harness, shooting to her feet like a furious little cat trapped in the small cockpit.

'What's the rush?' He looked up at her.

'I could hit you!' she said, breathing heavily. 'I want you to know I think that was pretty detestable.'

He stood up too, towering over her. 'You mean you were affected as strongly as all that?'

'You know how I feel about flying! To be at your mercy...'

'You're in more danger now,' he assured her.

'Why, what could you do *now*?'

'I expect something you would really dislike!'

It was humiliating and contemptible, but suddenly she was frightened of him. He was too near, and to make a joke of anything or smooth him down seemed impossible. There was something very different about him, his blue, heavily fringed eyes looking at her with this new unknown quality that acted on her like a drug. She couldn't seem to move, and he reached out a hand jerking her against him. Even though she was shocked she spoke first.

'What is this? A sort of *droit du seigneur*?'

'I hope it's worth it!' he drawled.

'Touch me and I'll scream,' she threatened.

'As a matter of fact, you won't. You care too much about your precious skin and I might just bruise it!'

She forced some spirit into her tone. 'Stick to the rules, Ryan. Even with this lowly subject.'

'Being dramatic as usual?' His hold seemed to tighten convulsively.

'You bother me!'

'I realise that, but it's entirely your own fault!'

Her breath was shortening painfully. She couldn't sidestep him or break away but endure it, shocked and slightly dazed to find herself paralysed by his touch. It was hardly to be borne, so that after a minute her defence mechanism was near perfect again and she began to struggle violently. His arm dropped to her waist, bending her backwards.

'It hasn't just occurred to me, you're a little savage!'

She gritted her teeth and said with leaden humour: 'I couldn't be more sober. I hate you!'

'One of these days I might take you seriously,' he said.

'I'd be glad if you would!'

'Take it easy!' He pinned her without difficulty and incredibly she leaned against him, going quiet. Her body seemed to have a life of its own, careless of the mind's direction. She would have a great deal of explaining to do to herself. 'Tell me you're sorry for behaving so badly!' Ryan said almost gently.

'I *will* not! How dare you provoke me like this!'

'Maybe I can't leave you alone!'

'No, please, Ryan!' She was begging at last, realising how strong he was and the deliberation that was in him. It was foolish now to play into his hands and she wanted to call an abrupt halt. Ryan was a man she couldn't handle at all. Carefully she lifted her head, staring up into his face, her dark eyes filled with a strange intensity. There was some matching shade of feeling in his own face. She was sure she wasn't imagining it. She put out a hand as though to ward him off and in the very next second he pulled her right into his arms with a kind of mastery that stopped all her protests dead. She was actually trembling, her body and mind so confused it seemed like a crisis in her life, her delicately boned face, haunted and passionate, for her feelings and reactions were stronger than wisdom and caution and her declared intentions.

She shut her eyes so she couldn't see him and he lowered his head, not sparing her, but kissing her as a lover with very little thought for her innocence or lack of experience. It was like delivering up her soul, leaving her defenceless with nowhere to shelter. He was too practised, too worldly, with a sensual brilliance that was awakening every last raw emotion in her, making it easy for her to arouse him as he was arousing her. Afterwards for many long nights she would hate herself, but her mouth opened under pressure and his kiss deepened. She dared not deny him or lose this rapt, black magic, this intimate physical ravishment that found her desperately caught up in its centre. She couldn't fix anything in her mind, for heat was burning through her veins, almost totally consuming her.

When Ryan at last let her go only her natural courage gave her any sense of reality. 'Don't ask me why you had to do that!' she began, unable to explain it to herself.

'I know you, that's all!'

'You didn't have to be so drastic!'.

'Anything to improve communications, Kylie!'

'Then think deeper. You're creating more difficulties!'

'The way you're talking, one could imagine you didn't like it!' he observed.

She skirted around his tall, lean figure. 'If you think I did you must be crazy!'

'You'll know soon enough!'

It sounded like a warning, but she gave no sign of having heard him moving towards the cabin door. She dared not risk another showdown and her thoughts drove her to give a stifled moan. Nothing was happening as she intended. She could still feel the touch of his mouth and her blood surged in awareness. Her whole life seemed devoid of truth if she was ready to let him treat her with such flagrant mastery, a living possession he could claim as his own. The thought chilled her reckless blood. There was only one way to regard it, as an insult and one that would not happen again. Ryan had done it deliberately, she realised, and if he imagined it would make any difference it only emphasised her purpose. Her eyes swiftly veiled, avoiding looking at him or accepting a helping hand, she jumped down into the late afternoon sunshine, the pallor of her face suggesting that he had perpetrated some new atrocity. Nothing could lessen her feeling of unnatural agitation, as if clinging to him, his hand shaping her nape she had finally betrayed herself.

Overhead the lorikeets flapped idly in the heat and as Kylie glanced away in the direction of the house, the jeep suddenly materialised. It was Christy, and she allowed herself to relax her fantastic panic. Christy would give her back her assurance. On him she would focus her chief attention until Rex, hawk-eyed and handsome, arrived. She would do anything to shatter Ryan's strange power over her, for the bitter realisation had come to her beyond her denial. He was clever, but so was she, and there was war between them.

The wind rippled through her hair and brought colour to her face. She half flew towards the approaching vehicle as if it were her salvation, aware, like a warning, that she was trembling in every limb. Ryan was a man of action and his will was very strong. Was this some new way he had planned to subdue her? He had done it with consummate ease. Her pulses were throbbing and she pressed her hand tightly to the base of her throat. She was ashamed, so ashamed that she had yielded to his passion. It hurt her, the driving force in him. She had always known he was no ordinary man. He had always made her feel a child, uncertain; now he had made her feel like a woman, and it was shattering.

The jeep flung to a halt and Christy jumped out, holding out his arms. Kylie went into them as though she sought peace there. Christy, looking down at her, knew what she longed for and gave her a great bear hug, almost cracking her fragile bones.

'Poor little Kylie!' he said, and swept her off her feet, whirling her round and round like a child.

'Christy dear!' she said, her great dark eyes full of an affectionate light. 'Put me down. I'm all grown up now!'

'Put her down, Chris, you'll make her ill!'

'There *is* a pallor to her face, for all those spots of colour,' Christy agreed. 'How goes it, Big Brother?'

'Fine!' Ryan brought his hand down on his brother's shoulder. 'Anything I should know about?'

'Jeff and I have been working like slaves!'

'Good. See you keep at it in the days to come.'

'Have a heart, brother. The more important thing is to keep Kylie company—also other things. Anyone can see I'm her favourite. Right, Kylie?'

'Right!' she said, and her soft little laugh had a caressing quality that she could not prevent. Somehow or other Christy interpreted it correctly, for he was able to control his excitement. Kylie's innocent allure could get her into trouble. Even serious difficulties and he was her friend. Once, years ago when she thought he was in trouble, she had almost killed herself trying to help him, perching on a branch and swinging right out into the middle of the river. It had taken quite a lot to get them both back to shore, but it had been his own fault for tricking her. Kylie was a gallant little thing and her life in so many ways had been hard. There wasn't anything he wouldn't do for her and he was more than half in love with her, but he could see quite clearly that she wasn't for him.

Her dark eyes seemed to be looking right through Ryan, so Christy turned and touched her ivory skin with his finger. 'Go and sit in the jeep. I'll put your things in. I can't wait to see your party dress. It seems cruel to give the other girls such stiff competition.'

'Kylie wouldn't be everyone's cup of tea!' Ryan said smoothly.

'Well, she's sure as hell Rex's!'

Ryan looked at his brother for a long moment. 'When did you see him?'

'He called in yesterday. He wanted to have a look at Storm Boy.'

'And?'

'I'm not a complete idiot!'

'I know you're not,' agreed Ryan. 'You're a good boy, that's why I trust you and leave you behind.'

Christy's smooth tanned skin flushed with pleasure. 'Thanks, Boss. He's a strange one, that Rex. Do you know he hates your guts?'

'If he does I don't care!' Ryan said crisply. 'I've told Kylie—you can see she's got her back turned—the less she sees of Rex the better.'

'I should say so! I don't trust him. I'll look after her, don't worry!'

'There's no need for both of you to act as if I'm not here.' Kylie said in a taut voice.

'Keep your cool, little one!' Christy called to her. 'Fiery little thing, isn't she? That's what makes Kylie so fascinating—her contrasts are endless!'

'Exactly!' said Ryan, and moved a little restlessly. 'Let's get up to the house. As for Rex, never let him take advantage of you.'

'I believe I've got his measure now!' Christy answered his brother seriously. 'I don't know how he can justify some of his actions. Deep down he wants to be one of us, but he can't. He's got to do what Uncle Gerald wants or be counted a failure. I tell you he made me pretty angry, going behind your back.

'Course, he knew you weren't here.'

'And you did tell him I'd gone to pick up Kylie.'

'Why, yes! I didn't think there was any harm in that.'

'No harm at all,' Ryan said calmly. 'Put the gear in the back. I'll drive. It was a good trip, but I'm longing for a drink!'

Christy moved off smartly and Ryan walked back to the jeep, his blue eyes blazing as if he was angry. 'Move over!' he said to Kylie.

'Do you really think you can discuss me with your brother? I'm not a child.'

'*Move!*' He shifted her briskly into her corner.

'Brute!'

'Will nothing ever curb your tongue?'

'Nothing. You're angry. What about, Rex?'

'Listen to me, Kylie!' he said in a deadly voice that bewildered her. 'You've never seen me angry. Don't spoil your record.'

'And I'll tell you too I don't feel bound to obey your orders. I must go my own way!'

'You'll go *my* way while you're under my protection. Don't think for a minute you're going to satisfy any of Rex's selfish passions!'

'You've never been fair to him!' she said wretchedly.

'That will do. I don't want to hear another word from you. And while I think of it,' he added, 'don't attempt to ride Storm Boy!'

'You know quite well I can ride anything!'

'God! It's a fight every inch of the way!' he sighed. 'I'm telling you, and I'm not *insulting* you, he's too strong for you. Ride him and you're in for a scare or worse!'

Christy came to the side of the jeep, his eyes narrowing. 'What are you talking about now?' he asked.

'I've just been told to keep away from Storm Boy!' snapped Kylie.

'Do it, darlin', if you value your lovely neck. That's one mettlesome animal!'

Kylie turned away abruptly, the flash of anger still in her eyes. 'I'll be interested to know what I *can* do!'

'That's easy!' Christy said, and laughed. 'Limit yourself to me. By the way, Ryan, Mother has planned a special dinner. I thought I'd tell you so you won't hurt her feelings.'

'What?' said Ryan.

'I know, I know. You don't mean to. You've got so many things to divide your attention. God, how that woman loves you!'

Neither Ryan nor Kylie answered. Kylie would have known anyway that no special dinner would have been planned for her. There was a tremendous difference between the conqueror and conquered. The miracle was that she was here at all, an unknown, penniless ex-employee's daughter. The desire to hurt as she had been hurt was strong in her. She lifted her head and found her brooding gaze trapped by a pair of sapphire blue eyes.

'Ready, Kylie?' Ryan asked, and some tone in his voice made her hand shake. Did he know every last thought in her head?

'Certainly!' she said coolly. 'It will be good to see your mother and Claudia again.'

'Shut up!' Christy murmured, patting her shoulder. 'You trouble people, Kylie, didn't you know? The look of you, the way you act. You're different, and people don't always understand you.'

'Surely *you* do?' she asked lightly, slipping her fingers through his.

'I know I don't, but I'll never give up trying. I guess Ryan's the only one who has ever known which way you were going to jump. Remember he saved your life!'

'I was not aware he *did*!' she said harshly, removing her hand.

'Listen, sweetie...'

'Leave her!' said Ryan.

From the lagoon to the river the swans were moving in a great flock. It was nearly dusk and the rhythmical, powerful beat of their wings sounded their approach. They all looked up at their beautiful flight as they moved in an arrow formation, their long necks outstretched towards the water where they would sink with a soft spatter and fold those great glossy black wings into perfect curves and re-shape their long necks into a lovely graceful line.

'Didn't the soul of Apollo pass into a swan?' said Kylie. 'My father used to tell me that!'

She had no idea how forlorn she sounded, how revealing her face. Kind-hearted Christy felt stabbed. 'You're just as enchanting!' he said gently. For an instant he too felt gripped by a nightmare morning when Kylie's father had been killed. It had had a disastrous effect on her.

'Look, there's the lead swan homing in!' she said,

and her voice sounded happier. 'Aren't they beautiful, almost immortal!'

'You're pretty indestructible yourself!' Christy said admiringly, determined to prevent his sister from upsetting her. Kylie wasn't Claudia's favourite person, but Claudia, like everyone else in the family, did exactly what she was told. It was Ryan who held her life and future in his hands and in some curious way they were very close. He didn't quite know what the bond was, but it was very strong. Kylie, too, did what she was told. Sovereign River had never been a very tranquil place and her coming would stir things up a bit. She had a special talent for it.

'Put your foot down, Ryan!' Christy urged his brother. 'I'm as hungry as a hawk myself!'

CHAPTER SIX

DINNER was in progress, but it wasn't a very festive occasion as far as Kylie was concerned. Elizabeth Langton sat at the opposite end of the table to her son, severely elegant and seemingly serene, but Kylie, sensitive to every look, was aware of her disapproval, although Elizabeth was making a valiant effort for her eldest son's sake. Ryan had adopted a certain attitude in her life and wryly Kylie realised they all had to fall into line.

The table was a vision, a glittering collection of crystal on tall stems, antique silver and the finest English bone china. The floral centrepiece was an exquisite blend of lilies in the same delicate pink, blue and ivory as the porcelain chandelier that bathed them in its light. Mrs Langton had gone to enormous trouble and everything was perfect. It was wicked really to intrude on the family, although Claudia had staying with her her dearest friend, Camilla Russell, a remarkably pretty blonde.

All through the courses Camilla continued to sparkle, laughing with eagerness, catching her full bottom lip between her small pearly teeth. She had the most engaging deep dimples and her honey-blonde hair swung about her ears in a curvy cap with frothy bangs. She turned her head constantly in her host's direction and her eyes spoke volumes of desire. Camilla would be accepted quite happily into the family.

Kylie sat toying with her wine glass, thinking she would excuse herself immediately after dinner saying she was tired after her trip. No one would miss her, except perhaps Christy. Her silky curls made a perfect frame for her delicate face and her drowned dark eyes, and her dress was a beautiful shade of amethyst matching the gemstone on a fine gold chain around her neck. Looking up suddenly, she encountered Camilla's pale blue glance and unaccountably she shivered.

'It's lovely to see you, Kylie, after all this time,' Camilla said sweetly. 'I'm sure you find plenty to do as a teacher.'

'I enjoy it!' Kylie said, smiling.

'I had no idea teachers looked like you,' Camilla said innocently, her eyes flickering.

'What's that supposed to mean?' Christy asked. 'I

once had a woman teacher—a most beautiful lady!'

'I only meant Kylie is ... exotic!' Camilla explained herself, as though exotic was neither fitting or helpful.

Kylie drew a deep breath. She was conscious of Camilla's antagonism and it seemed absurd to her. If only she knew! Christy poured a little more champagne into the beautiful Waterford wine glass.

'Drink up, Kylie. This is supposed to be a celebration.'

'Besides, I have something planned for us later.' Ryan looked around the table.

'Tell us?' Claudia swung her head, her long brown hair cascading silkily over one shoulder.

'The wizard man is going to allow us to witness one of the ceremonial dances!'

'How come?' Claudia asked in surprise.

'Ryan helped him out, of course!' Jeff murmured dryly. 'He was practically dead when Ryan found him—snakebite.'

'Now he's going to let us watch the dancing?' Claudia's blue eyes flew to her eldest brother.

'They're expecting us.'

'How marvellous!' said Camilla, possessed by the idea of being out in the starlight with Ryan.

'You'll excuse me, won't you, dearest?' Elizabeth asked him. 'After all, I've always found these affairs amazing.'

'That's perfectly all right. We might have to stand anyway.' Ryan's blue eyes looked along the table to Kylie. 'You're very quiet. Some fresh air will do you good.'

She wanted to say she didn't want to come, he was

observing her so sharply, but Christy took hold of her arm. 'Don't be afraid—I'll look after you. These ballets sometimes end in a frenzy!'

'If they do I'll scream!' Camilla cried like an excited little girl. 'Ryan, I'm going to hold tight to your arm.'

'Why not hold on to mine!' Jeff offered, and reached for her hand. 'How about it?' There was a jaunty smile on his face and Camilla declined charmingly:

'Another time!'

'I'll hold you to it!' He looked straight at her and his young, good-looking face hardened amazingly.

In that moment Kylie considered he had a fleeting resemblance to Ryan. Three of Elizabeth Langton's children had taken after her side of the family, indeed Claudia was supposed to be the image of her mother as a young girl; only Ryan was a Langton, bearing a closer resemblance to his uncle Gerald and his cousin Rex than either of his brothers. Kylie sat there and watched them. Christy had already told her Jeff was currently enamoured of the quick-witted and ambitious Camilla, but apparently he wasn't having much success. All the same, he was very attractive and persistent in his own fashion. Claudia, Jeff and Christy all had light brown hair easily bleached by the sun and sky blue eyes, and being Elizabeth's children they were all good-looking, but a stranger would have found it impossible to link them with Ryan. They were very much like their mother and one another. Ryan was the odd one out, Indian-dark with the dazzling shock of jewelled eyes.

As they got up from the table Claudia remarked

quite civilly on the pretty colour of Kylie's dress, but her glance said quite plainly that it didn't bear a label worth mentioning. Kylie didn't care; she was secure, at least, in her own beauty. Claudia was a frightful snob and so was Camilla with her pretty, patronising manner. They really did think the world was turned on for them, and Kylie was forced to admit that perhaps it was. Neither girl worked for a living, but they found plenty of things to fill up their time. Christy came to claim her and she felt herself brushed by Elizabeth Langton's cold blue eyes. There was guarded disapproval in their icy depths and Elizabeth looked away abruptly and turned to her eldest son, the change in her expression remarkable. Ryan was the great love of her life, and Kylie watched him say something to her, then lean down and brush her cheek with his mouth. Poor Elizabeth! There wasn't much of her son's time spared to her. She idolised him, yet somehow gave the impression that she went slightly in awe of him. There was none of the quiet control and authority she exercised over Jeff and Christy or the prideful affection she lavished on Claudia.

It was a glorious Outback night, the air so pure and dry the stars blazed prolifically, brilliant like flowers strewn all over the sky. The earth and the sky seemed limitless and the spirit drums drew them to the appointed spot for this hitherto secret dance ritual. It was a great honour and Ryan had given them to understand clearly that they should appear suitably appreciative, with the three girls deliberately effacing themselves. Male supremacy was a powerful factor in the aboriginal way of life, and women were excluded from many of their rites.

Dakka, the wizard man, came out of the trees to greet them, his body paint and feathered headdress rather frightening to Kylie's mind, and she saw Camilla shiver and fall back against Ryan's shoulder. Dakka had been on the property for more years than anyone could remember and he was a fearsome old devil with his dilly bag full of charms and the ghastly, extensive cicatrices or ritual scarring all over his emaciated body.

He pulled a parakeet feather from his headdress and passed it to Ryan, who answered his jabbering with a few words in dialect. The glittering old eyes covered each of them in turn, then he pointed back to the trees where a group of sacred dancers were sitting around a blazing fire staring at it until they were almost dazed. The drum sounds were being made by young initiated boys, and though they were soft now Kylie knew they could rise to such a crescendo to echo miles away in the hill country. There were no women or lubras or plump piccaninnies present, and from his impatient leaping actions Dakka was anxious to get underway.

They stood until the dancers fell into squads, then Ryan motioned to them quietly to sit down on the grassy knoll overlooking the small circle of fires. Dakka the wizard man and the central dancer put the palms of his hands together above his head and began to sway in time to the tap sticks, then the other dancers joined in with rhythmic movements. There was no audience participation invited, they were to sit there and witness this symbolic dance handed down from who knows when.

The firelight danced on the painted bodies, the tufted cockatoo and galah feathers in their headbands.

Dakka was leaping about like a cat on burning bricks
and in full view of everyone he picked up a shovel-
headed spear and began to gesture with it, so suc-
cessfully that Kylie felt a shadow of the old terrors
when wild marauding blacks had wandered the coun-
tryside. There were plenty of them there, in among
the trees, each one of them admirable with a spear. In
the old days Dakka had been a great warrior and perhaps he was even dreaming something up for them
now. Kylie had known him since a child and he was a
crafty and cunning old devil and had been in his
virility a ritual killer.

She was coiled up like a kitten, her dark eyes huge,
and Christy pressed her arm gently, silently cautioning
her to relax. The taint of goanna fat rose from the
heated, writhing bodies and she was glad of the
heavily scented brown and yellow flowered boronia
that grew so prolifically in the bush. The dance was
apparently a revenge dance about a giant spirit, an old
man and a hunter who wandered about the country-
side seeking members of a rival tribe so he could drag
them away and kill them. Three of the dancers had
already fallen prostrate, mortally wounded. Dakka was
now stamping and leaping with all the vigour and
elevation of a young man, the other dancers moving in
a completely different style, the accompaniment of tap
sticks and sand drums harshly exciting. Kylie had seen
many dance sequences, mostly with women playing
an unobtrusive part, but never had she seen such a
dramatic and indisputably aggressive performance.
Dakka, the major figure, was creating a very real giant
spirit hungering for blood and he was even crying to
himself, totally taken over by the mythical being he

was portraying. One rival warrior, braver than most, was circling the wizard man to the rising crescendo of the drums, not cowering away from the threatening spear, when suddenly a nightjar in its silent flight gave a piercing, reeling call almost directly over their heads.

Camilla couldn't help herself. As a reaction against the rhythmic frenzy of the dance she laughed sharply and in an instant all she could hear was her own gasping breath. The dancers, the primitive musicians, came to a twitching halt, their black eyes flashing with outrage. An insult had been offered. Behind her back Kylie felt Christy's uneasy breath. Dakka was scowling like an animal, glancing back, and Camilla's little moment of bravado had turned to fright. She had interrupted the climax of a sacred dance. Perhaps they wouldn't rest until she was punished. All around them was the still and vast bush.

Like a panther Ryan sprang up and grasped Kylie, jerking her to her feet like a rag doll.

'Start to whimper!' he urged her, and the pressure of his hands almost made her do just that.

Dakka was padding towards them, the shovel nosed spear still in his hands. Ryan didn't move, but held Kylie firmly between his hands. All of them knew the spell of the dance was broken and Dakka, still the primitive, was softly lashing them with his tongue. Her heart drumming, Kylie began to whimper most piteously, huddled against Ryan's towering figure. A dreadful quietness prevailed and Dakka's eyes told them he was furiously angry. In the days gone by he wouldn't have taken such an insult so easily, but as he met the Big Feller's eyes he knew he wasn't able or capable of taking vengeance. Besides, and they could see from the shrug of his incredibly thin shoulders, he recognised Kylie, who had attended the dances since she was very, very small.

He peered suspiciously into her woebegone face and she lifted her eyes briefly and beseechingly. It was then Ryan spoke, explaining how she had been carried away by the dance and had cried out her fear. It was unforgivable, but it was explainable. Women were weak, silly creatures, and see how abjectly she begged for forgiveness. Behind them, Camilla had turned faint and Jeff took the opportunity to comfort her. Camilla was a young girl Dakka didn't know and she had no gift for acting and downcasting her eyes.

Kylie, however, looked a small figure of dread, so much so that Dakka reluctantly became himself again, offering to finish the dance, but only if the foolish young girl who had dared to laugh was banished instantly. Ryan offered to remove her and Dakka trudged back silently to within the circle of fires waiting for the Big Feller to return from the estate car that had brought them.

They couldn't run, but Ryan paced her very quickly towards the big safari estate car. "You won't be frightened, will you?'

'Does it matter? That was altogether an enthralling performance.'

'I couldn't have let him point the finger at Camilla,' he said dryly.

'Oh no! I assure you I was only too ready to die in her place.'

'Don't be a little idiot!' He kept his hand on her shoulder. 'Camilla would have gone completely to pieces. She hasn't your dramatic flair. Anyway, the old devil knows you. The whole thing will die down easily now. It was a great honour, you know.'

'And pretty stupid of Camilla to laugh. It beats me why you brought her.'

'Don't you worry. She'll spring back amazingly. In fact I shouldn't be surprised if she turns out the heroine of the whole piece. This kind of thing goes over big in the city.'

'So I've found!' said Kylie drily.

They reached the car and he opened the front door. 'Get in, like a good girl. It shouldn't last much longer and I'm expected to be there.' The interior light came on and his blue eyes held her dark ones. 'Lock yourself in.'

'What on earth for?' She shook her had slowly. 'Besides, it's too hot. Go on, you go. I've given you all the assistance I can.'

'Let's talk about it another time!'

'No!' she said sharply. 'No. No. No!'

He looked at her calmly, his dark face a mixture of amusement and mockery. 'Every picture tells a story. You're not really irresistible, you know. You just have a great face!'

'And you have a rare arrogance!'

'Take a spell!' he drawled, his blue eyes moving over her. 'I'm going!'

The next morning Kylie was up early for her morning ride. The sun gilded the tops of the trees and the breeze crooned a shivery song through the trees. There were moments in her life when she was completely happy, and this was one of them. The birds whistled and shrieked and sang and even the kookaburra's wild cackling call seemed wonderful. Sara would find the bird life sensational. She had once kept two little budgies in a cage and thought that splendid. Now in the azure and gold of the morning thousands were wheeling in tight formation, more compact little birds than their brothers bred in captivity.

By the time she got to the creek there was a lot of activity about the property and she had to wait until a large mob of cattle forded the crossing, two coloured stockmen in attendance. They lifted their wide-brimmed hats and Kylie waved as she steered the bay gelding along the bank. Finally it was her turn to cross and once up on the flats she put the bay to the gallop, full of confidence and exhilaration. She had no particular plan in mind, just a therapeutic ride. She would have loved to be riding Leura, Ryan's pure white Arab, or the extraordinary Storm Boy, but the gelding was a beautiful goer, well-bred and high-strung, sharing her delight in the morning. Kylie was a natural in the saddle. She had been riding from early childhood and she had no fear of horses nor they of her. Even the violent manner in which her father had died made no difference. Her sweet mouth compressed with dry humour. Camilla had an unholy fear of anything four-legged. Kylie considered she could help Camilla, but of course she would never be invited, and Claudia had too much respect for her friend's sensitive feelings.

Once the gelding's first exuberance wore off, Kylie steadied him down to an easy walk, once again experiencing the sense of awe and affinity she had with this vast, empty land. Small green water plants marked the deep blue of a shallow swamp, that dried out between rains, and beneath the mulga scrub the blood red earth was thickly carpeted with transients, white, gold and pink. Even in drought the hard seeds survived to flower the desert with the least drop of rain.

A rider came out of the avenue of trees and she reined to a halt, watching him, though she felt inclined to gallop away. There was no sense in openly confronting Ryan, but here on Sovereign River she had to live his way. Under the shadowed brim of his stetson his blue eyes were glowing with a startling depth of colour.

'Hi, you're out early!'

In spite of the hot sun Kylie felt herself going shivery again, and he walked the Arab right up beside her. 'I said, *hi*!'

'I heard you. I just can't get my breath.'

'Maybe it's too difficult for you, our paths crossing.'

'It's your land!' she pointed out dryly.

'Yours too. Are you under some vow of secrecy?'

Some face-saving instinct made her look him right in the eye. 'I can't think what you mean.'

'You always know what I mean, Kylie!' he corrected her. 'You've just got to pretend you don't.'

She didn't deny it, but leaned over and patted the Arab's neck. 'Good morning, my beauty!' Leura responded to the petting as she always did and Kylie smiled. 'Aren't you flawless? Fit for the Royal Jordanian stud!'

'I'm not sure you don't prefer horses to people!' Ryan remarked a little soberly.

'I do!' she returned shortly.

'I thought Christy was going to join you.'

'He wanted to, but I'm very happy by myself.'

'Would you like me to ride on?' He took the gelding's reins and held them.

Her delicate brows drew together and she hit his hand with the butt of her riding crop. 'I don't give that much for your tricks, Ryan Langton, and I'm not going to be plunged into a cheap affair. Not with *you*!'

'I wasn't aware I invited you to. At the same time, I don't mind repeating that particular trick. It seems to be the only way I can reach you.'

'Why ever would you want to?' she murmured inaudibly.

'Why won't you look at me?' he asked.

'I want to keep my pleasure in the morning!' She looked directly at him then, seeing the flooding mockery in his eyes. It was useless to pretend there was nothing between them. The weight of his mouth lay on her like a burden. She even imagined he could see its imprint.

'Idiot!' he said in a gentling voice.

'Can you really read my mind?'

'Right now, the two of us are thinking the same thing!'

'The devil we are!' She struck him away severely and the gelding, insulted by the slight slap of her crop, shot away in startled response.

She didn't expect him to come after her until the Arab flashed past her. 'Do you want to break your neck?' he shouted.

His voice carried quite clearly to her and she gave up the mad chase. Something had driven wisdom from her. The gelding was prancing and chewing, still full of run, but they were moving into more difficult

terrain. Ryan came up beside her again and she could
see from his face he was angry.

'What a reckless little fool you are, Kylie. You were
going too fast to pull up easily. The bay is dead fit and
you were giving it its head.'

'Don't tell me how to ride!' she said mutinously.

'Watch it!' he returned curtly. 'I just might turn
you over my knee.'

'Something a gentleman would never do!'

'My dear Kylie, I'm compelled to tell you you don't
act like a lady! You simply don't realise the chances
you take. The ground is pitted with melon holes—you
only have to look around.'

'I'm sorry!' she said shortly, shaking her head to set
her curls free.

'Do you think I'd enjoy it to see you maimed or
worse?'

'Why not? Maybe my family were cursed.'

'Cursed be damned! Why won't you let go of the
past?'

'I'm trying!' she said, and looked into his lean, dark
face. 'You might pay that a little more mind!'

A faintly bitter smile played around his mouth. 'I
don't intend to meet you head-on in a quarrel—
anyway, not now. Christy seems to have followed after
you despite your wishes.'

Kylie turned her head with relief saw that this was
so. Christy was whirling his hat around and they could
see his teeth white in his tanned face. 'He's greatly
attracted to you!' Ryan said shortly. 'Don't hurt him.'

'Doesn't it shock you that I might?'

His blue eyes were piercing. 'Nothing about you

could shock me. I'm just telling you you'd be making
a mistake!'

'Well, don't get in a state about it!' she goaded him,
feeling curiously tranquil, the more so because Christy
was almost upon them.

'But you don't know at all how I feel!' The smooth
taunt put her teeth on edge. 'You see, Kylie, I'm
certain you're going to get what you deserve!'

Christy reined in beside them, his eyes going from
one to the other. 'Not storm clouds, surely?' He spoke
with humour, but his eyes were shrewd.

'Not really,' Kylie answered sweetly. 'It's just that
Ryan and I can't take more than a few minutes of each
other's company.'

'Agreed!' Ryan murmured with irony. 'Keep the
little firebrand company.'

'I'd be absolutely delighted!' Christy said in a dashing fashion. 'I'm weak. For me, Kylie's company is
like wine.'

'Forgive me if I plead a headache!' Ryan returned
suavely. 'You've got an hour to dally, and after that I
want you to meet me down at the Five-Mile. It's a
long day ahead and Kylie told me herself to give you
more work to do.'

Christy struggled with his surprise and lost. 'Is that
right?'

'I don't know why he should have told you, but yes.
You could make more of an effort, you and Jeff.'

'Darling!' Christy said firmly. 'Anything to gain
your approval. It's very nice of you to take an interest.
I like it. Perhaps you could give me a few tips.'

'I think I'd have to take the complete day off, and

Ryan wants you in another hour.'

'Oh well, I've no doubt you'll make the most of it!' Ryan touched a hand to his hat in salute and rode off.

'What's with you two?' Christy asked gently.

Kylie turned back and faced him. 'I've already told you—we're incompatible.'

'I've heard of it, but my dear, it's not that!'

'Where shall we go?' Kylie asked after a moment. 'I so enjoy a morning ride.'

'Obviously you have the advantage of poor little Camilla. She's a bit embarrassing, flinging herself at Ryan. At least Laura is never as silly as that.'

'I like Laura and she happens to like me. I can't say the same of Camilla. She didn't even say thank you for helping her out of a sticky situation last night.'

'It was a damned silly thing to do,' said Christy. 'I can't see why Jeff's so smitten.'

Kylie looked at him and smiled. 'She *is* very pretty!'

'She's not a patch on you.'

'So *you* say. Each man to his taste!'

'It might be a kindness,' Christy said calmly, 'if Claudia tells her she doesn't have a chance with Ryan.'

'Never mind!' Kylie said briefly. 'There's nothing in his manner to suggest he finds her a bore. He might well be enjoying it.'

'Yes, we might as well face it. He's got plenty of sex appeal, but I for one am not going to lie down and take it. Just so long as he doesn't take an interest in *you*.'

'Don't be such a fool!' Kylie's small face wore a

look of proud indifference. 'Are you coming with me or not?'

'Of course I am!' Christy said, astonished, unaware that he had said the worst thing of all. Kylie could be totally unexpected at times...

The rest of the morning Kylie passed up the pleasure of the station's huge, inground swimming pool for the deep reaches of the river. She had her own favourite waterhole, and in any case Claudia and Camilla had no need of her company. Their acid little remarks were like stones that never quite hit her, and Camilla had shown her annoyance that Kylie had some brief conversation with Ryan that morning.

It was beautiful at the pool, overhung with feathery enveloping trees, the water crystal clear and quite cold even when warmed by the sun. Kylie dived and swam, her head spinning with her own thoughts, then afterwards lay stretched out on the sand, a sprite who had come up from the jade depths of the stream. The brief scraps of lycra that made up her swimsuit were many shades deeper than the thick towel beneath her and her small breasts and limbs had the perfection of a statuette. The minutes lengthened and she luxuriated in the heat of the sun after the chill of the water. It was just what she needed.

'Hello, darling!' a voice said behind her, and she sat up like a startled doe, instantly alert.

'Rex!' she exclaimed.

'How goes it, my lovely!'

For a moment her mind refused to function. 'What brings you here?' she asked.

'A damned silly question!' He moved down the bank towards her. 'You, of course.'

'Should I be flattered?' She looked around in vain for her sundress, but it seemed to have melted from sight.

'Why not? I'm a lot in demand.'

She could not have moved to save her life, so surprised was she by his sudden appearance. 'How did you know where to find me?' she asked, holding her hand before her eyes, so large did he seem.

'Good old Liz!' He dropped down beside her, his face full of a hard sensuality that she could hardly fail to be aware of. 'She has to protect the love of her life, so any diversion will do.'

'You mean she sent you down here deliberately?'

'Exactly!' His bluish-grey gaze ranged over her fragile, sweetly curving body. 'Liz doesn't favour beautiful small girls who might entice her son away from her.'

'Which son?' Kylie asked, without looking at him directly.

'Is there more than one?'

'She loves them all!' Kylie said flatly.

'Does she?' he mocked her. 'But how, little Kylie, in comparison with the almighty Ryan? Where is he, by the way? I wouldn't like a punch in the nose.'

Her hair was a silky whirl about her face and her eyes were huge. Rex, she knew, was capable of pulling her to him, to twist her in his arms and perhaps conquer his own fascination. There was no honour in Rex but tormented arrogance. No tenderness or protectiveness, but the primitive instinct to reach out and take what he wanted, especially a forbidden challenge.

There was a strong resemblance to Ryan in the lean height and the Langton chiselled features, but some darkness and faint malevolence in Rex made him forever walk in Ryan's shadow.

'What a pity you're not at all suitable!' he said gently, and slid his hand around her nape. 'I'd seriously think of marrying you.'

She flared up and flung his hand away. 'Oddly enough, I'm not interested.'

'Maybe you're just teasing?'

'You only recognise what you want to. Besides, no woman is important enough to wreck your future. Your father might disinherit you if you stepped out of line.'

'Maybe!' he nodded, and his eyes were ugly in his face. 'He was bitterly deprived of his own heritage.'

'It's so damned easy to think that, but you could be wrong.'

Rex struck his knee with his clenched fist. 'But this is unbelievable! I know you've no loyalty whatever to Ryan.'

'On the contrary, I shall always be grateful to him.'

He seized her hand and looked into her face, his expression almost comical. 'What are you saying? It's not possible you've changed.'

'You're hurting me, Rex!' she said evenly. 'Incidentally, you were asking where Ryan is. There's a ceremony over at Leila's grandfather's place. It's time for his soul to depart the house, and Ryan had to attend.'

'The Great White Chief, of course!'

'Something like that. I imagine your father has to do much the same thing.'

Lightly and playfully he pulled one of her curls. 'Then it should take him the best part of the day.'

'Chris is around!' Kylie said pointedly, disliking the look on his face.

'Good old Chris! Ryan's little watchdog!'

'Chris is my friend!'

'So am I, babe!' he said patiently. 'What beautiful skin you've got—flawless except for that little beauty spot near your mouth. Tell me, pretty one, why are you here?'

The parrots squawked as she got up to look around for her sundress. 'For Claudia's birthday,' she answered casually.

Rex gazed back at her with an odd expression on his face. 'Claudia is wishing you a thousand miles away!'

'Who cares about Claudia!' Swiftly she pulled the silky shift over her head and twitched it into place.

He laughed with bitter humour and pitched a stone into the river. 'Don't we all do as we're told? All except Dad and Ryan, that is.'

'Someone has to be Boss,' she pointed out.

'One of these days I might be!'

Kylie's heart was warm for all her cool poise. 'I hope so, Rex,' she said gently. 'You need to be free.'

A slight flush crept into his darkly tanned face. 'Come back and sit beside me—I'm not dangerous. Have you ever thought, Kylie, if my father were dead I might get around to asking you to marry me?'

Kylie shrugged and sat down near him on a boulder. 'Why would you do that? You're not in love with me.'

'Who says I'm not? I'm not, as a matter of fact, but

you fascinate me. You're a very seductive little thing, Kylie, hasn't anyone told you?'

'They may have,' she shrugged. 'I don't take all that much notice.'

'No, you're not vain, just a natural. How's the water?'

'Cold. Very bracing. I prefer to be away from the house.'

'It can't be easy for you without the Big Man around. He's well and truly appointed himself your keeper. What's with you two?'

'Absolutely nothing!' she said violently.

'That's what I mean.' He looked at her with narrowed eyes. 'You've always exploded about Ryan and he's always played it mighty cool with you.'

'Why go over old ground?' she protested, tossing her head. 'I remember you did it the last time.'

'That's the first time it struck me. You're not a little girl any longer. Things change. Ryan's got himself a very beautiful ward and he knows it. He's got quite an eye for beautiful things, as you know. Why, these days you look more expensive than all the others put together. Just how well does he keep you?'

'He doesn't keep me at all!' she said shortly, indignation colouring her cheeks. 'I work for my living and my father's estate provides a small allowance.'

'Oh, come off it!' he said crudely. 'An allowance? How naïve can you get? Your poor old dad didn't have a cracker!'

'How the devil would you know?'

'Oh, come on...'

'My father had saved a tidy sum, a *miserable* sum by your standards, I suppose, but Ryan invested it.

You know he's brilliant at that kind of thing. He has all those mineral shares himself in Mount Caradine.'

'So that's the story he told you?' Rex murmured sardonically.

'It's no story. He was telling the truth. I don't want to discuss this, Rex.'

'Of course you don't. You might get at the truth. Ryan has been keeping you for years, very nearly in the lap of luxury. Your dear old dad didn't put you through university.'

'I'm going to ignore you!' she said positively.

'I can't very well ignore you,' he retorted. 'Your eyes flash when you're angry, sparkling like great jets. I think I like black eyes the best of all. Where do you get that strange foreign look?'

'What's strange about it?' she asked heatedly. 'Maybe *you're* strange.'

'Now, now, don't get angry. I'm on your side. Any time you want to exchange me for Ryan will be just fine.'

'In what capacity?' she asked scathingly.

'I'd see you were rewarded.'

'How insulting! Ryan doesn't reward me.'

'Has he ever made love to you?'

It seemed bitter and twisted the way it came out and Kylie reacted with impatient disgust. 'I find this whole conversation unacceptable,' she said coldly.

'Has he?' Rex persisted, tightly grasping her arm. 'I think he has. Maybe only a little, but he's held you in his arms and kissed you.'

'Let me go!' she said with exaggerated quietness.

'No. You've too little experience!' His voice became urgent. 'You talk about problems—I think you have a problem with Ryan. You've been in love with him for years, Sleeping Princess!'

'You're mad! I hate him!' she cried, beginning to get excited.

'Little fool! Why don't you hate me like that? Fight me if you want to—I like it!' He twisted one of her arms behind her back and held it. He was laughing and he was very strong. Kylie didn't want his kiss, but she did want to know why her body still burned with the memory of Ryan's mouth on her own. She appeared to relax without yielding and Rex gave a harsh exclamation, pulling her right into his arms and catching her mouth with his own, devouring her so that she soon found it unbearable. There was too much hunger and too little control, a fierce male passion and a singular lack of feeling for her own response.

She struggled to break free and he wrenched her hard against him, his taut face dark and attractive, the blue-grey of his eyes deepening. Desire without love— she knew it was only that. But he wanted her desperately and she could feel the betraying tremble in his body. In a struggle her frail strength would be useless, and Rex had been sent here by Elizabeth Langton, that perfect lady.

'Let me love you!' he whispered intensely.

'Let you rape me, you mean!'

'You might like it!'

'Never *ever* believe it. There's only one way a woman will ever truly accept a man, and that's with love. All else is desperation.'

'And what are you so desperate about?' he asked harshly. 'Ryan?'

'You're hurting me and you're beginning to turn ugly. I know you would. You hate him, don't you? Your own cousin. You even look a little like him.'

'He doesn't exactly love me!'

'You have the answer to that—your father. He's always promoted bad feeling between you. The blame is his, not Ryan's.'

'Why the little champion?' jeered Rex. 'What's happened to all that famous hostility? Bogus, like I've always suspected.'

'I'm only speaking the truth. I don't have to lie about him.'

The sun fell upon her, illuminating her eyes and her hair and her skin. The scent of lilies clung to her skin. She had never seemed more erotic to him and he was quickly losing control. 'Ryan will never be your lover!' he said through clenched teeth.

'He'll never be invited.'

'You don't understand yourself, do you?' he asked with hard awareness. 'You're a man's woman, a real woman. You could entice a man away from everything he believes in and wants. I tell you it could be all right with us. Find out what it's like.'

She tried to turn her head away from him, but he caught her chin, letting his fingers roam over her moulded mouth, then pressing down to her small teeth. 'Does it shock you to have a man touch you? You're practically a child, for all your superficial sophistication!' There was a fine tremor in his hand pointing to the violence of his underlying feelings and Kylie was beginning to be frightened. This was just such a situation as Elizabeth Langton might have expected, a deliberate attempt on her part to place Kylie at some kind of risk. Rex was long used to meeting with compliance. With so much in the way of good looks and money, his inherent ruthlessness did little to turn eager young women away.

His hand slowly circled her shoulder, caressing, drifting lower to her tilted breast. She couldn't bear him to touch her there, like a violation. She was entirely her own woman, yet Ryan's hand had shaped her blossoming body. She couldn't rationalise anything. She could only get away from Rex, who was greedy and obsessed, his eyes a hard, bitter blue and not brilliant like sapphires.

'I want you!' he said in a weighted, faintly slurred voice.

Kylie pushed against him helplessly, almost obscured by his powerful frame. His arrogance appalled her and his hold was painful, almost brutal. He was totally absorbed in himself and the pleasure she was giving him. She could scarcely move her arms, but she still had the use of her legs. Frantic now, she kicked forward blindly, using the sudden advantage the moment gave her. It seemed like the hardest thing she had ever had to do, but she was away from him now, and running, her body sprung to quivering life. Tears were spilling helplessly on to her face and she managed to wipe them away. If Rex wanted to, he could overtake her; he might even get a great kick out of it. Something sharp scraped her bare foot, but she kept moving, naturally fleet of foot, straining not to be recaptured.

It was all so sordid and so inexorable, woman at the mercy of a man's brutal strength and drive, only she was no sad and pitiful creature. Her body was on edge with outrage. There would be no sweetness to that seduction, only shame. He was coming after her, his long legs quickly covering the rising ground. He didn't call her, but he was drawing nearer, and with her ultimate burst of speed she drew to the top of the small grassy hill overlooking the deep pool. Her pulses were jumping and her legs trembling, yet she glanced backwards and saw him and the silent unconcerned way he was coming after her. Her own breath was ringing in her ears and there was nothing even remotely disturbed about him.

'What are you running from? Stop and think!' he called to her.

A few seconds later a man's voice rang out. It was Christy's and it filled her with relief.

'Kylie?'

Rex's smile seemed strangely sinister. 'Funny he should turn up now,' he drawled.

'I'm bloody glad he did!' she said, and didn't apologise for her language. 'I don't want your attentions, Rex, and I've never encouraged them.'

'You're just going to take a little longer, that's all!' He was frowning, his head lifted, and he looked dangerous.

'Damn, damn, damn!' Christy was yelling, crashing through the bush. 'Kylie, where the hell are you?'

'I'm here!' She rested against a blossoming bauhinia, lifting her voice to reach him.

'Drat you, girl!' Christy came into sight, visibly perspiring. 'I've been told to keep an eye on you!' He shook his head and came to a stunned halt. 'Rex!' A glaze came over his eyes and he even lifted his fist.

'Didn't you know he was here?' Kylie asked

quickly, forcing her voice to lightness. 'Your mother sent him down to fetch me.'

'*Mother* did?'

'Anything unusual about that?' Rex asked sardonically, moving up the bank to join them. All of the Langton men were over six feet, yet Christy looked a boy beside him.

Christy remained grave, looking from one to the other. 'You all right, Kylie?'

'Of course I am. I've had my swim.'

He looked at her searchingly, sensing something was wrong. 'Where are your things? Go and get them.'

'Listen to the boy giving orders!' Rex drawled.

'What are you doing here, Rex?' Christy challenged him. 'I didn't see you come in.'

'Then what brought you here on the double? Obeying Big Brother?'

'Why not? This is our property and as far as I can see you're a trespasser!'

The situation was swinging out of control and desperately Kylie tried to save it. 'I've hurt my foot, Christy,' she said plaintively.

'How?' he demanded with difficulty, resisting the impulse to lay his cousin flat.

'I cut it on a stone. Rex,' she turned to him and tried to speak normally, 'are you coming back up to the house?'

'Would *you*, after you've been insulted?'

'Then why don't you clear out?' Christy yelled.

'Don't bug me, boy!' Rex said contemptuously.

'It's time someone did!' Christy growled, with no back-down at all.

'Neither of you have any sense!' said Kylie shortly. 'If you won't get my things, Christy, I'll get them myself.'

'Allow me!' Rex bowed suavely. 'You two stay here holding hands!'

He moved off with controlled grace and Christy moved back up the bank to where Kylie was standing. 'What the hell was he up to?' he demanded.

'I told you—your mother sent him down here to fetch me.'

'That doesn't make sense!' Christy murmured, his brow crinkling. 'He's got a thing about you, and he's no gentleman!'

'He's not like you, Christy, but I can handle him.'

'He's not what you're used to, Kylie, and his feelings go deep. He'd do anything to score off Ryan— you must see that. Don't for God's sake encourage him. I'm only trying to be helpful!'

'The warning's unnecessary,' said Kylie. 'I know him!'

'Then tell Ryan,' Christy exploded.

'I won't be telling Ryan anything. There's nothing to tell. Your mother sent him after me.'

'I can't believe it!' Christy said, convinced his mother was above any kind of suspicion. 'She doesn't know Rex at all. He's not a very pleasant fellow. A lot of things aren't right around here You could at least have covered yourself up a bit. I mean, that swim-suit...'

'Be that as it may, I thought I was on my own. He only turned up a few minutes ago and he's coming back now. Please don't start anything, Christy. It's important you don't upset your mother or Claudia.

He's family and he's been invited for the party.'

'That was Mother's actual doing. I'd like to kick him and his old man to Kingdom Come!'

Kylie pressed his arm, too spent to talk any more, and Christy turned his head and looked down at her. He heaved a sigh and flexed the muscles in his back and shoulders. It was obvious Kylie didn't want him to do anything, and it was acting as a deterrent even when he felt positively maddened. Rex could probably knock him rotten and he was sure to be a dirty fighter, but the sight of Kylie's pale face was making Christy function at top gear himself. Something had happened to upset Kylie, and he knew pretty well what it was. Had his mother lost her senses, sending Rex after Kylie? Everyone knew Rex's reaction to Kylie, just as they knew his general strategy. Kylie was no hardened sophisticate, but a fastidious young girl, and Christy determined he was going to protect her even if it proved painful.

Rex came back up to them carrying Kylie's towel and her beach bag. 'I know what you're thinking, boyo, but don't even try it. I'll be damned if I'll bruise my knuckles on you.'

'Pass me my things!' Kylie said loudly.

'How about a thank-you?' Rex's glittery gaze shifted.

'Thank you.'

'Fine!' His eyes slid right over her. 'No one likes to leave a lady out on a limb.'

Beside her, Christy stiffened, and she snatched at his arm. 'It might be a good idea if we all went back up to the house.'

'I don't care one damn about going back,' Rex said

coolly, 'but just as you wish, little Kylie!'

He followed them at his leisure, full of disdain for Christy, the watchdog, and an undiminished passion for Kylie that he was determined to assuage. It would be really something to take Ryan's little ward!

CHAPTER SEVEN

THE house and the vast perimeter of the grounds was ablaze with lights. It was Claudia's twenty-first birthday party and it was a success before it had even started. Most of the rooms in the magnificent old Georgian mansion had been opened and a lot of the guests afterwards said they had never seen anything like it, for Edward Langton, who had begun this rich cattle empire, had built on the grand scale and commissioned one of the finest English architects of his time to draw up the plans and specifications. To visit Sovereign River, the great station and the homestead, was a unique experience, and to see it when it was *en fête* was to fully appreciate its beauty and style, the quality of life the wealthy colonial families had surrounded themselves with.

The great reception rooms, richly decorated and almost unaltered from Edward Langton's day, looked extravagantly beautiful with their crystal chandeliers and giant gilt-framed mirrors, the beautiful furnishings and the paintings, the opulent ornamental detail of the plasterwork, the lavish use of blue and ivory and gold against the gleaming french-polished woodwork of the great double doors and the magnificent T-shaped staircase that rose to the gallery. The whole effect was superb and the firm in charge of the floral arrangements, given such a setting as the house and a fabulous collection of vases and containers in every shape, size and ware, whether silver or copper or antique porcelain and glass, had achieved the most spectacular effects which would come under discussion for months to come and rate special coverage in the leading women's magazine that was to cover such a grand social occasion.

The station staff were not to be without their own celebration, and the huge sales shed had been turned into an excellent ballroom with long tables set up at one end for a lavish buffet and naturally plenty to drink. No one outside Ryan seemed to know exactly how much it all was going to cost, but it was certain it was going to cost a very great deal. Miss Claudia Langton of Sovereign River had reached her majority and no expense would be spared. Ryan had already presented her with his own present, an exquisite set of diamond and aquamarine pieces which she was to wear that night, and she would probably look brilliant, for she had been in a fever of excitement all day.

Inside her room, almost dressed, Kylie was caught up in a wave of nostalgia. No parties for her. No mother or father. No loving brother to cover her with diamonds and lavishly entertain all her friends. Then she controlled herself. She couldn't think of her father now or even her mother. She couldn't indulge in useless self-pity. It was Claudia's party and it would soon be over. She was in a strange mood and she was trembling slightly. Ryan had scarcely spoken to her in two days, nor since he had come home to find his cousin Rex there. He had flown her and Laura into Adelaide and been perfectly charming to the poor girl who adored him, but to Kylie he had shown a disconcerting remoteness. Even anger she would have welcomed, but not this hardened indifference. Unlike Christy, he had given no indication of his feelings towards his cousin, yet somehow he had managed to have Rex off the station the very next morning, and all done with the smoothest affability. Ryan was a diplomat, and that obviously rattled Rex considerably. So clearly the master of all he surveyed, Ryan often gave the impression that he was only humouring the lot of them, and his cousin both feared and respected him. Even that afternoon, his team soundly beaten in a quickly organised polo match, the muscles of his jaw and throat clenched, Rex had leaned over his pony's neck and shaken Ryan's hand, the victor. It was a gesture he was required to make, but tension had lingered in the air.

Kylie hadn't even wanted to go, though she normally enjoyed these matches, but everyone went along as a matter of course and her absence might have been remarked on. It was quite an exciting match. They were all dashing horsemen, but Ryan as usual caught everyone's eye, a bold and formidable player, and his cousin was furious and obliged to hide it. It was most unfortunate, the one-sided rivalry, and it reached its height in the final chukka. Kylie had been glad when it was all over, though everyone declared it had been one of the most exciting matches they had seen for a long time. They would still be discussing it that evening and the outstanding quality of play. Even the hidden and unsuitable fury on Rex Langton's lean, dark face, betraying all the old family feuds and history, and they were all shamelessly watching for some signs of it. The stories about the Langton brothers, Richard and Gerald, had been legion, repeated over and over. They all knew something of the extraordinary situation and the stories had been added to in the next generation. In many ways it was hard on Rex, being outclassed by his cousin, but there was some treachery in Rex and now and again it showed very clearly.

Kylie, so weighed down by her crazed sense of duty to her father, should have been concerned for herself. In the times they had been thrown into one another's company, Rex's eyes hadn't moved off her. Such intensity, such a waiting watchfulness might have frightened another girl or had her protesting hysterically, but she scarcely seemed to see him. There were many things she didn't know about herself, and now she was wretched over Ryan's curious attitude. He had always taken such notice of her even as a child, and she had become used to it and couldn't rest until he noticed her again.

Wearing her beautiful opal-coloured dress that was cut very low and revealed the delicate swell of her breasts and the flawless quality of her skin, she was shocked and horrified by her own thoughts. She hated Ryan, didn't she? He was responsible for her father's violent death and the pain and loneliness she had endured these long empty years without him. A million shivery sensations brushed her spine, thoughts of being made love to—by only one man. Nothing made sense.

Her hair was a shining mass of curls around her small proud head, her dark eyes huge, her mouth deepened to a dark iridescent rose, blusher delicately applied to her delicately modelled cheekbones. She was looking her very best, but there was no look of pleasure or triumph in her eyes. They were bewildered as new thoughts and feelings kept filtering through her brain and inner voices whispered to her what they had never said before. The shimmering chiffon outlined the fragile contours of her body. She turned this way and that, but could find no fault. There would be many beautiful women there that night, consciously dressed to their most brilliant, wearing fabulous jewellery.

She bent forward to stare at her Victorian amethyst necklace on a fine eighteen-carat gold chain. It was very pretty, matching the flare of opal colour in her gown, and it was the best she could do. For the first time in years she was too thoroughly intimidated to ask Ryan for her opal. She would rather have gone without adornment than to approach him in his present mood. No doubt he thought she had developed a reckless passion for Rex and was taking satisfaction in flaunting it. Rex had made it appear that way, and tormented by her own thoughts, Kylie had unwittingly added to the impression. Rex was a devil who wanted what belonged to his cousin, but even now she wouldn't take him seriously. She would be safely surrounded tonight. Nothing could happen with so many people in the house. Besides, Rex's father would be there to watch them all with his strange burning eyes, eyes that had once been as vivid a blue as his nephew's.

When a knock came at her door Kylie went to it slowly. Nothing would ever make her warm to Elizabeth Langton again. She hoped it was neither she nor her daughter, and she couldn't see why it would be either. Ryan stood in the doorway, devastatingly handsome, his evening clothes faultless, his chiselled features and tall elegant frame never seen to better advantage than now. His blue eyes were dazzling in the polished dark bronze of his face, but they weren't in the least kind or admiring.

'May I come in?' he asked sardonically.

'It's your house!' she said in automatic rebellion.

'Cleverly hidden tonight. I've never seen so many strange people in it. Turn around and let me look at you.'

'Don't concern yourself! I'm dressed quite adequately!'

'I said, *turn around!*'

She did so with astonishing abandon, her eyes firing at the crisp tone of his voice, her long flowing skirt swirling out in a peacock cloud. 'What's the matter, Ryan? Are you afraid I might disgrace you?'

'What a temperament you've got!' he murmured almost casually. 'Tell me, do you practise in front of your mirror?'

Soft lights cast a rosy glow over her ivory skin and gleaming black hair. She looked very beautiful and strangely vulnerable. 'What is it?' she almost pleaded, oddly disturbed by his presence in her room.

'I've got something for you. That necklace is pretty, but it simply won't do.'

'I'm not likely to accept another!'

'Oh, *won't* you?' He stretched out his hand and she

backed away from him.

A flash of amusement lit his face and he gave the ghost of a smile, just a glimmer of white in a darkly tanned face. 'Now's as good a time as any to tell you you remind me of a high-strung filly!'

'What a strange man you are, Ryan!' she said, fascinated and hardly able to look away from him.

'The worst kind, Kylie, because I always get my way!' He tilted his head to the side, examining her critically. 'You look ravishing, but I've something that will do you better justice. Come here, little one. This is a great evening for my sister and I'm not going to let you spoil it.'

She gave him a strange look of reproach. 'I swear I don't want to do that!'

'Things have a way of happening when you're around!' he remarked dryly.

'Then why have me here?'

'I'm beginning to ask myself the same question!' He delved inside his inner breast pocket and withdrew a necklace that glittered and gleamed in the light. 'This is your father's opal,' he said by way of explanation. 'I've had it put into a suitable setting and I think it will go perfectly with that dress.'

She stared at the lovely thing almost in horror, for it was suspended from a string of brilliant cut diamonds and diamonds clustered around the large black opal that flashed its jostling fires of emerald and purple and amethyst and crimson. Kylie continued to stand there almost stricken and Ryan went behind her, unfastening the necklace she wore and placing it on the dressing table before slipping the opal pendant around her bare ivory throat, his fingers barely brushing her skin, yet searing her vividly.

She didn't know how she felt. She didn't even know if he was insulting her because he was so rich. She didn't lower her head or attempt to look at herself, and his hands closed over her shoulders to turn her towards the cheval glass that was tilted to the right angle and reflected them fully in its long mirrored panel. He looked splendid and insolent, too tall and too powerful for her. She closed her eyes, knowing she was swaying, and he drew her back hard against him.

'You work too hard to hate me, and it won't come!'

'I've always believed it!' she muttered.

'Have you? I just wouldn't let it happen.'

'I can't wear this, Ryan,' she whispered. 'Everyone will know where it came from.'

'Does that matter?'

'Yes, it does!' Her eyes flew open and she seemed to come back to herself. 'Why did you do it?'

'Easy!' he said. 'It's a fine opal. It deserved the right setting, and I like you to look beautiful.'

'I'm not going to say thank you!' she said, her heart twisting over.

'I realise that. I know all about you, Kylie, and it frightens you, doesn't it?'

'You must remember you've known me since I was a child.'

'And you were a handful even in those days!' His blue eyes swept her. 'By the way, I've marked Rex and his intentions. It's no time to be stupid. Keep away from him tonight even if you're longing to make trouble!'

'And I know the way!'

'Of course you do. Quite definitely. But, Kylie, the one you're inviting trouble from is *me*!'

She smiled at him, a miracle of exquisite, bitter enchantment. 'You're the only one I'm interested in!'

'Do you think I don't know that?'

She stared at him in longing and loathing, excitement pulsing through her veins. 'It's you I want to suffer. Down all your days!'

'Poor Kylie!' he said, his sapphire eyes glittering under the lids. There was a hard, mocking quality to his voice that hurt her and reduced her words to scented breaths.

'Oh, go away!' she said fiercely, realising with a pang that she was utterly absorbed in him, the imperious set of his head, the curve of his beautiful mouth, the whiplash alertness about him.

'For you, Kylie, *anything!*' he said with a faint bitterness. 'You'll need to be a good sweet little girl tonight or anything will come of it!' He walked away to the door, then turned back to look over his shoulder. 'Just remember, I'll be watching you like a hawk!'

'Then expect trouble!'

His blue glance struck her and a soft shiver ran down her spine. She moved back quickly and clasped the poster of the bed, twining her arms around it for support. Fate had played too many terrible tricks on her to feel this tormented yearning. She couldn't bear it, or the pounding of her stormy heart. How could she want to hurt him and yet fight the craving to go into his arms?

'Well, I did warn you, didn't I!' His blue eyes were very steady, very cool. He watched her for a moment longer, then he shut the door.

★

Kylie should have been enjoying herself enormously, but she was too conscious of the undercurrents and the effort involved in eluding Rex's determined advances. She could tell that behind his smooth, smiling face he was very angry. Jeff had rescued her at least three times, but now he had succeeded in prising Camilla away from a circle of admirers. Camilla looked lovely, like a spring flower, and Claudia was very much the privileged young lady, loved and admired, her beautiful white dress floating like gossamer, her blue eyes as bright as the aquamarines around her neck. As she passed to and fro, people lifted their glasses and saluted her, and she responded with more charm and animation than Kylie had ever seen.

Kylie was just waiting for her partner to return to her when Elizabeth Langton passed near. It was impossible for either to ignore the other.

'Enjoying yourself, my dear?' The light eyes were as cold as the magnificent diamond brooch on her silver gown.

'Very much, Mrs Langton. You must be very proud of your beautiful home and your handsome family.'

'Yes!' There was a slight flush on Elizabeth's high cheekbones. 'We do know how to put on grand occasions such as these.'

'Claudia looks beautiful,' Kylie remarked sincerely.

'Yes, she does look very well. Camilla, too, a very sweet girl!' For the first time Elizabeth looked at Kylie properly. 'Where *did* you get that remarkable necklace?'

'Surely you know the opal's history? My father mined it himself. It's quite valuable.'

'My dear!' Elizabeth's eyes hardened. 'It could

easily have swung from a plain gold chain!'

'It was Ryan's idea,' Kylie said unwisely.

'And I shrink from knowing his reasons!'

'Don't let me keep you any longer, Mrs Langton,' Kylie said calmly. 'I know how you'll want to see if everything is going smoothly.'

Elizabeth smiled and as she was a tall woman she towered over Kylie. 'I don't think it necessary for you to dismiss me in my own home. You're a dangerous young girl—I've always said so.'

'Be comforted, Mrs. Langton!' Kylie said soberly. 'I won't be here all that much longer.'

A blaze of anger went through Elizabeth, deepening her flush. She swept away, fighting to retain her cool composure, and as she did she saw Rex elbow his way towards Kylie.

Kylie was suddenly so upset from her encounter with Mrs Langton that she let him sweep her into his arms. He looked very tall and handsome in his evening clothes, not unlike Ryan when seen from the back with his dark well-shaped head and wide-shouldered, lean body.

'Your father might see us,' she said, 'and he won't be pleased!'

'Tonight I'm a free spirit!' Rex pulled her even closer to him. 'What was Liz saying to you to make you go pale?'

'Just the usual things a queen says to an expectant little nobody.'

His mouth twisted into a smile. 'You'd be a fool to attempt to get into this family.'

'Mrs Langton was kind enough to tell me.'

Rex's embrace grew more demanding. 'What about Chris? His intentions seem honourable.'

'Christy is my friend. Nothing more.' Kylie looked up at him, expecting her expression to speak for itself. He was treating her like a doll he was about to crush. 'You're holding me too tightly.'

'So?'

'If you don't ease your grip I shall kick you in the shins!' She smiled sweetly as though they were the best of friends.

'Hello there!'

Laura drifted past, amazingly elegant in a pure green silky jersey Kylie had picked out for her. Her hair was drawn back smoothly into a full chignon and pinned with a hand-made silk rose.

'You look gorgeous, dear!' Rex drawled rather cruelly. 'I didn't recognise you, in fact!'

Nice Laura didn't appear to take offence. 'I hardly understand the transformation myself, but I'm very grateful!' Her eyes met Kylie's and the younger girl smiled.

'What was all that about?' Rex asked later.

'Nothing much. Laura and I went on a shopping spree together.'

'I *see*!' Rex whistled beneath his breath. 'Get her away from that bitch of a mother?'

'There's too much to admire in Laura. I just thought she needed a little help.'

'She'll need more than that to replace Liz as mistress of Sovereign River. Camilla's doing *her* thing in typical fashion. Liz isn't about to surrender to either.'

'What do you want in a woman, Rex?' Kylie asked involuntarily.

'Surely the usual things!' His eyes dropped to the shadowed cleft of her breast.

'A heart and a mind?'

'So long as they go along with the right body—and it's no use bending yours away from me. Someone might notice. It's all very splendid, isn't it? Dear little Laura deserves the best. A very lively gathering. Mamma even pulled out the old oak chest in case Liz's jewellery was better than hers. Haven't seen much of Ryan, have you? Of course they've all got to pay homage,' he went on, 'and he's got to spread himself around. It's almost like a royal occasion. This is a fabulous old house, isn't it?'

'Yes, it is!' she agreed gently, because there was something faintly pathetic in his longing tone.

'Picture yourself mistress of it?'

'How could I ever be called to such greatness?' she said dryly.

'Well, Ryan has to marry. They all seem to fling themselves at his head, but he can't want any of them badly enough. Laura's been slightly crazy about him for ever, and I must say she looks rather stylish to-night. What's this I hear about Ryan racing his own horses?'

'I know nothing about that!' Kylie said in a low swift denial.

'I think you're lying. Of course I can't prove it. Sure you're not concealing a dark secret? You're just the girl to do it!'

'I told you—I don't know.'

'And I don't believe you!' he said flatly. 'You're a cold little thing, aren't you? You won't let yourself be loved.'

'Corrupted, you mean.'

He glanced down at her and his smile was sharp. 'Don't say things like that or I might slap you.'

'I wouldn't advise it, not with everybody watching. Why me anyway, Rex?'

'Because you're Ryan's little girl!' he said brutally.

'And you'd get pleasure out of hurting him?'

'I had the impression that so would you,' he shrugged.

'If I could do so, now, with you, I *wouldn't!*'

'And what's behind it, Kylie?' His dark face looked ruthless.

'Nothing. A woman's nature.'

'Don't give me that!' he said jeeringly. 'Women are cruel, crueller than men. Take dear old Liz, now, with her frozen well-bred face. She wouldn't care how I treated you.'

'Then she would have to deal with her son.'

His pale eyes narrowed. 'You sound very sure of yourself, very secure. I don't think you realise how far I'd go!'

Kylie went to swing out of his arms, but the orchestra started up once more. 'What a pity to waste such passion, Rex. If you must upset the applecart pay some attention to Laura. Mrs Langton doesn't *disapprove* of her and her father is very, very rich!'

'That's about all that saves her. She's sexless!'

'She's charming,' Kylie said sharply. 'Only you can't see beneath the skin.'

'I'd like to see all of *your* skin,' he said deliberately. 'That's how I picture you—without this dress. One day I'll know.'

She let her arms fall, but he still held her tightly about her narrow waist. 'You don't really fool me with that cool little don't-touch-me. Underneath you're as sensual as hell!'

Some of her apprehension came from the fear of a scene. They could hardly remain there like that, and suddenly they didn't have to. Ryan was at his cousin's shoulder, and he wasn't a man who showed his emotions on his face.

'May I?' he asked, in a smooth controlled voice.

'Certainly, cousin!'

'You never miss a chance, do you, Rex?' Ryan said coolly, and steered Kylie back into a crowd who were casting surreptitious glances over their shoulders, awaiting further developments. A little scandal always added to the enjoyment of an evening.

Nothing happened. Rex melted away and nothing more out of the ordinary was happening than Ryan Langton claiming his first dance from his Cinderella ward. A little to the left of them Camilla laughed indulgently at something her partner was saying, but inside she flamed with an unnatural violence. Men like Ryan Langton were greatly to be prized, exceptional individuals, and she could have punished Kylie for claiming his attention.

It's strange, Kylie thought, the way our bodies flow together. She didn't dare look up into the dominant dark face above her, but said much as a child would:

'I think Rex is quite mad!'

'And you, of course, have to stoke up the fires!'

'I did nothing. I was actually trying to behave myself. I can't think why.'

'*I* can,' he said dryly.

'Then why come to my aid?'

'You looked so damned obvious. You don't really deserve help. He's right about one thing—there's a storm of intensity in you. It's very intriguing, sheltering behind that aloof little face.'

'What else did you hear, I wonder?'

'Nothing. Which is as well, judging from the colour under your skin. I'll wait my moment with Rex.'

'I think his main trouble is that he's misunderstood. He *can* be charming.'

'Like a rattlesnake. Go nowhere alone with him.'

His voice sounded grim and she leaned away from him. 'Aren't you forgetting I'm all grown up?'

'I hadn't particularly noticed,' he drawled.

'*Rex* has!' she retorted.

'You never flag, do you?' One hand slipped along the curve of her back. 'I know you're ripe for your first affair, but don't think of having it with Rex. Another thing, don't reveal yourself to malicious eyes.'

'Gossip spreads even without support. Besides, everyone loves talking about you Langtons!' Her eyes ranged over the other dancers. 'Doesn't Laura look lovely?'

'I nearly passed her without recognising her!' he answered with humour. 'Both of you are to be congratulated. Laura's a very nice young woman. A bit slow in maturing.'

'Then why don't you cultivate her?' she asked.

'You'll have to give me a better reason than that.' A brilliant mocking light flared in his eyes.

'What have you got against marriage?'

'Nothing at all,' he said briefly. 'I know what I want and who I want. I'm just waiting until she can tolerate the thought.'

Kylie tilted her head and looked up at him, her large, tilted eyes sparkling with malice. 'Not *you*, Ryan,' she mocked him. 'There's not a woman in this room who wouldn't jump at the chance, eligible or not.'

'Does that include you?' he asked suavely.

'Please leave *me* out of it,' she said ironically. 'I'm the rare one with a built-in immunity.'

'So why are you trembling?'

There was a hard, mocking quality to his voice that hurt her. 'It's your incurable effect on me!' she returned with forced lightness.

'Poor Kylie,' he said quietly. 'You've been very lonely in your prison.'

Her heartbeats seemed to be shaking her. The music swirled all round them, drowning her in sensation, and she couldn't prevent it. Sensations that were surely doomed. Everything about him filled her with tenderness and violence, an ache and a longing. She had to be mad.

After all, it was her one and only dance with Ryan the entire night. He took Laura in to supper and afterwards there was always some pretty girl clinging to his arm, staring up into his face with gleaming, challenging eyes. Kylie wasn't sure how she managed it, but she too kept a changing line of partners in thrall. The ball would go on for ever and a splendid breakfast would be served in the formal dining room for all those that had the strength to appear for it.

Shortly before two, Kylie went upstairs to repair her make-up. She wasn't sure how many bedrooms there were in the house, but all of them were being used. The sound of music floated up to her and she moved along the rose-gold of the softly lit corridor like a winging bird. A hand came out from an open doorway and grasped her, and despite herself she gave an exclamation of fright.

'Oh, Christy!' The fright abated and she stared at him.

'Sorry, sweetheart, did I startle you?'

'You did rather,' she admitted.

There was an added lustre on him in his evening clothes, his dark golden skin slightly flushed. 'You're not going to bed, are you? I've hardly been able to get near you all night.'

'We had supper together, didn't we?' she smiled.

'What with McCleary on the other side and no way to get rid of him? I was just fetching this photograph for Mother. The Senator wants to see it. It's one of the few Claudia had taken with Dad.'

'Poor Claudia!'

'That's the story!' Christy said gently. 'Dad never saw anyone but Ryan. You know that. I know that. Ryan was the sun, moon and stars, the man of the future. The rest of us didn't really count.'

'You're a very good brother, Christy. I'm very fond of you.'

'*Fond!*' He groaned in disgust. 'I'd give anything to change that. From the moment you came downstairs there wasn't another girl in the place!'

'I'm not going to believe that,' she said. 'I saw you with Patti Morgan.'

'Patti's too interested in a wonderful meal ticket!' he said cynically.

'Don't underestimate your own attraction. Patti's father can buy her everything she wants.'

'But not for ever. A girl has to find herself a good man of her own.'

'That's essential, isn't it?' Kylie smiled at him and, carried away, Christy drew her back into his mother's huge, beautiful bedroom, encircling her slight body with his ardent young arms. 'Couldn't you care about me, Kylie? I'd do anything for you.'

'*Please*, Christy,' she said gently, unwilling to hurt him.

'You're terrific!' he insisted.

'No, Christy,' she said firmly.

'I've had too much champagne, I know, but you're the sweetest girl I'll ever know. I don't want a silly little butterfly, I want a real woman. Why, you even ride as well as I do.'

'*Better*,' she said, frowning. 'Now stop this, Christy.'

'I'm going to get the name of that champagne and order a case. Let me kiss you, Kylie. I can't go on wondering what it would be like.'

'I tell you,' she said sharply, 'we have to get out of your mother's bedroom. I can just see her withering disapproval.'

'Don't be too hard on Mother!' he whispered into her silky neck. 'She's right to be frightened of you.'

'Frightened of *me?*' She drew back in astonishment.

'Yes, you.' He held her dark eyes. 'Kiss me and we'll go. Don't be cruel, don't deny me. I've dreamed of kissing you for a couple of years now.'

'And you might suffer for it!' She pushed against him, her mood changing.

'I don't care.' He held her easily. 'It will be worth it. I'm breathless already. Please, Kylie. You'll never be sure if you don't try it.'

His hand snaked out and grasped a handful of her curls, then he bent his head to find her mouth with surprising expertise. It was so sweet, she half surrendered because of her special feeling for him. He was an intensely engaging young man and he was very good at kissing. She was even faintly laughing, which lent him an extra abandon and he lifted her up to his shoulder so she wasn't even touching the ground.

'There, that wasn't so bad!' he grinned.

'No, it wasn't. You're very attractive and you've had a large quantity to drink.'

'Don't talk down to me,' he begged her, his voice husky with emotion. 'You're such a *little* thing!'

He dipped his head again, but a third voice behind them snapped them both out of their half dreamy conversation.

'And you're a goddamn fast mover!'

The sheer violence of the tone made Christy deposit Kylie none too gently back on the floor. He swung about, keeping an arm around her, a storm breaking over his sunny, enraptured expression. 'What the hell are *you* doing up here?'

'Chasing up Kylie. Just like you!' Rex regarded his cousin contemptuously already half way across the room.

'I like that!' Christy exploded. 'I was fetching something for my mother.'

'Isn't that cute!' Rex tipped his head to one side. 'Fetching something for Mummy!' He snapped an insolent glance at Kylie. 'I have to hand it to you, girl, when you look at a man, you really poison him!'

Christy found this remark so offensive he aimed a punch that should have gone straight to his cousin's jaw, but Rex's left hand shot up like steel, deflecting the blow while the other hand hit out hard and fast, smashing against Christy's vulnerable chin. He staggered and fell back, cracking his head against the brass-studded antique chest that stood at the base of the four-poster bed.

'Dumb ox!' Rex pondered the prone figure briefly.

'What a swine you are, Rex!' Kylie ran to the fallen Christy, her face showing her distress.

'I'm sorry I'm not entirely to your liking, ma'am, but you sure as hell are to mine!'

'Go away—I loathe you!' she said violently.

'That doesn't make a great deal of difference. I can cure you of all your little tantrums. Leave him alone. He's all right!'

'He's out cold!'

'So what?' Rex moved swiftly, jerking her to her feet. 'I'm trying to be patient, Kylie, but your time's running out.'

'When is it going to dawn on you that I'm not interested?' she muttered violently.

'*No!*' There was a pinched expression on his face. 'I've noticed who interests you—the master of the house. Don't waste any time making plans there. You'll never be his equal. Leave it to the ultra-sophisticated birds downstairs. This is as good a chance as we'll get to be together. You won't have a hard time, I promise you!' He was holding her elbows and she flung out her hands, her nails curling.

'For once you've made an embarrassing mistake!' she snapped.

'But do you *mean* it. Go on, I don't mind if you claw at me. You're so little, but I can't go carefully with you. I want to settle this now and you're very much to my taste. Stop it, Kylie, you might get hurt if you struggle so hard.'

He was handling her effortlessly, pinning her so she was helpless. 'Do you realise this is Mrs Langton's room?' she said desperately.

'It's hard to miss it with all the gear in here. Doesn't she just love playing queen of the castle? That would be some adjustment handing it over to you!'

'You're mad!' she gasped.

'Oh, I don't know! Ryan has a soft spot for you somewhere in the granite heart.'

'He wouldn't be doing *this!*'

'Oh no, he's far too much the gentleman!' Desire was leaping in him and he tugged at her hair painfully, pulling her head back. 'Tell me what you want and I'll give it to you.'

'A million wouldn't be enough!'

'Little bitch!'

Kylie, facing the door, saw Elizabeth Langton first. She stood braced in an attitude of frozen disgust, her voice when she spoke splintering into fragments. 'I would very much like an explanation!'

'I'm sure there's a good one!' Rex said suavely.

She made an imperious dismissive gesture with her head. 'I realise Kylie doesn't know any better, but you must be losing your mind, Rex, to come up here like this.'

'But.Aunty, my date was waiting!'

Elizabeth stared at his dark sardonic face and her mouth twisted in outrage. 'What you do elsewhere is none of my business, but this is *my* home and *my* bedroom!'

Kylie moved and for the first time Elizabeth saw her son. Her eyes glinted oddly and her tall figure was convulsed.

'Christy!' She sounded like a demented woman and Rex offered offhandedly:

'Take it easy. He has a bump on his head and a sore jaw. That's about all it amounts to!' He barely glanced at Christy's prone body as though he didn't merit his attention.

Elizabeth went down on her knees, and Christy chose that precise moment to groan and turn over. 'Christy dear, speak to me!'

Christy let his breath out and gave another groan. 'A truck hit me. I'm sure it was!'

'Come on, Kylie!' Rex reached for her. 'We don't have to wait. Liz and I never did hit it off for any length of time.'

'What have you done to him?' Elizabeth cried despairingly.

'Nothing much. He was lucky. Actually he took a swipe at me. I was merely defending myself—the innocent bystander.'

Rex's hand tightened on Kylie's shoulder, urging

her forward, and Elizabeth glanced back at them, her voice like a whiplash.

'Over Kylie?'

'She's quite a challenge!' Rex smiled. 'Don't be fooled by her fastidious little air. Those dark eyes are as beautiful as a deer's. She knows exactly how to entice a man!'

'What a pity she had to be caught doing it!'

The frigid contempt was too much for Kylie. She jerked away from Rex's hand, her eyes beginning to blaze. 'You can be quite certain I came up here alone. Christy was fetching the photograph you wanted and he was coming back downstairs when I passed him in the hall.'

'Hah!' Rex gave a mocking jeer, his own emotions not quite under control. 'I thought he was devoting most of his time to kissing you. Don't let her fool you, Liz, she's dangling all your sons on a string!'

'Not if I can prevent it,' said Elizabeth icily. 'Under no circumstances would I consider you, Kylie, in any capacity. You really haven't been as clever as you think. I don't know how you ever came to gain such a foothold in this family. Your behaviour is typical too!'

'So is yours!' Kylie returned violently. 'You're a cold, arrogant woman and you've never properly developed your own personality. You're only half alive. There's very little you can hold against me, but it gives you a sense of power to keep me in the place you fancy I belong. You've never had any real power. That's something the Langton men have—your husband, now Ryan. I know what he means to you and I feel sorry for you. Your life has been one long search for love. You're not going to abandon your son, are you? He's all you've got!'

'You're not making sense!' Elizabeth said with hardened contempt. 'There's always been something very strange about you!'

'Yes, I understand the truth. You don't like that. You like to live behind your frozen mask, as I do. When did you discover your husband didn't love you?'

'How dare you!' Elizabeth got to her feet with a mighty effort, her face like paper.

'I'd dare more than that,' said Kylie furiously. 'When are you going to stop this oppression? You can't go around arranging marriages. You think yourself so perfect when all you know is exactly what type of woman will let you remain here and earn your son's undying devotion. It's pitiful, and I've done nothing to earn such hateful rejection. But I'm not worth your kindness and you've never troubled to waste it on me. How could I deprive you of your wonderful son? You want to decide who's going to do that.'

'For God's sake!' Rex shook his head in irritation. 'I don't want to listen to all this. It's such a bore. Who cares for her plans? All women make 'em. Come with me, Kylie.'

'I will now!'

For an instant all the years of rejection claimed her. The roar of humiliation thundered in her ears. Rex at least was honest. He was a rake and he said so. No woman would ever enslave Ryan, and she cursed her woman's heart. Women were fools, starved for love. Not only Elizabeth, who had only known her husband at a distance for all their four children. She herself was just as bad; the forsaken orphan looking too high. She had to be out of her mind, and she felt overwhelmingly tired. She didn't hear Christy speak to her. She was lost in her own agony. Such bitterness—she couldn't suffer it from Ryan's family. Her own thoughts of vengeance, the old grief and despair that had haunted her, had blown away on the wind. Now only love ravished her and it would follow her about for a long time.

Rex was waiting with his hot blue eyes. Greedy, handsome Rex with his own form of cruelty. How was it possible to take his hand? Incredible even for a moment to have thought of it. His eyes were fastened on her face and his smooth smile was unpleasant. He cared nothing for Elizabeth's white face and the pulse that beat in her frail temple. His eyes were all for Kylie, using the situation for his own ends:

'I knew you'd show a little sense!'

'Get her out of here!' Elizabeth ordered in a hard, low voice.

'Why not? We can go somewhere alone. My father doesn't give a damn provided I come back.'

'Then he must be as low and detestable as you are!'

They were all of them abominably startled. Ryan was in the doorway looking across at them grimly. In some extraordinary way, though there was nothing outwardly violent about his voice or expression, Kylie began to tremble uncontrollably. Simultaneously Christy, who had been lying in dazed mortification, jumped to his feet, supporting his mother whose fine skin had whitened to parchment. His expression was one of iron control, but the blue eyes had an annihilating blaze.

'I didn't think it would be necessary to come upstairs to call back half the party, but since I'm here, you might give me the whole story. Christy, we'll start with you!'

'Nothing to worry about!' Christy said hastily, his concern divided between Kylie and his mother.

'I'll decide what's going to worry me!' Ryan said curtly.

'Mother sent me up to get that photograph of Claudia taken with Dad. You know, the one when she's up on Blue Flash.'

'Go on.'

'Kylie was on her way to her room and I spoke to her—that's all. Rex for some reason followed us up, then Mother when I didn't return smartly enough. That's all there is to it!'

'And it's very hard to believe. Your jaw is swollen and the skin is starting to discolour already. Rex hit you, didn't he, and no one has returned the compliment. As yet.'

'Then you know also he was annoying Kylie!' Rex interrupted, a faint flush on his high cheekbones.

'Christy annoying Kylie?' Ryan turned to regard him.

'He was kissing her senseless when I came up to see what had happened to her.'

'And for this reason you knocked him rotten?'

'Somebody had to!' Rex reproached him. 'You weren't here.'

'Shouldn't we go back to your guests?' Elizabeth Langton murmured painfully. 'We can discuss this later.'

'Yes, we can.'

'You look so angry, Ryan,' she pleaded. 'Kylie will always bring unhappiness wherever she goes.'

'Perhaps your knowledge of happiness is limited,' he said gravely. 'I know you don't understand her and I know you take your life of luxury and protection carelessly instead of the great blessing it is. Kylie has been starved of love and safety for most of her life, yet she could never show the deliberate unkindness of those who have an absolute belief in their own privileged position. I've sworn to look after you and I will, but a lot of things will be stopped.'

Elizabeth's smile was distressing to see. 'She's turned you against me, hasn't she?'

Ryan studied his mother with almost impersonal eyes. 'There's no way she could do that. You have my love and my loyalty, but there'll be many things that won't happen again. Go downstairs, Mother. Claudia's party has been a brilliant success. Don't spoil it after all you've done. I know you always behave perfectly whatever your feelings.'

Abruptly Rex broke into laughter. 'She wasn't behaving too perfectly just now—in fact she was shrieking at Kylie to get out. She hates her, didn't you know?'

'Why should she?' Ryan's face was hard and controlled, the face of a formidable man. 'Just think about it, all of you. Why should she?'

'Of course I do not!' Elizabeth Langton bowed her handsome head. 'Please, Ryan, the only way now is to forget it all. Christy dear, what can we do about your face?'

'He can go to bed,' Ryan said shortly. 'No one will miss him. He's had too much to drink anyway.'

'That's O.K.!' Christy couldn't deny it.

'Well then, that's settled nicely!' Rex murmured in his languid drawl.

'Not quite!'

Ryan's voice was deceptive. He seemed to move like a panther, half springing across the blue and gold room, permitting himself the luxury of literally flattening his cousin, who went down with the thud of a fallen oak and remained rootless on the carpet.

Frightened, Elizabeth looked back at her son, but he was only adjusting the cuff of his shirt. He looked as tall and elegant, as polished as a man could be. The hardness hadn't gone completely from his face, but his mouth had relaxed. His brilliant blue eyes hovered for a moment on his cousin, then he turned and looked at his mother, nodding his head.

'Go downstairs, Mother. There's nothing at all for you to do here. Don't worry about Rex either. Nothing bothers him, does it, Rex? You can take it as well as dish it out!'

Rex sat up, but he didn't open his mouth.

'All right!' Ryan turned away. 'Christy, call it a night. I'll make your excuses. When you come down most of them will be gone and the rest always like a good joke. Think of one.'

Rex picked himself up like a character in a Western, dusting himself off elaborately and playing the part to perfection. 'I guess I had that coming!' he shrugged.

'That and more!' Ryan agreed promptly, quite prepared to swing again.

'You must see I had cause,' Rex added. 'Kylie is dazzling!'

'But she's never smiled at *you*!'

'Funny, that!' Rex smiled with difficulty. 'It's not often I want a woman to.'

'Are you coming, Rex?' Elizabeth asked bluntly, appalled with his behaviour and for the first time in her life uncertain of her own.

'Why, certainly, Aunty. I guess I'm lucky I wasn't beaten up.'

'Then you'd better stay at a distance in future!' Ryan said crisply.

'You've finally convinced me!' Rex turned back to regard his cousin. 'I can't help admiring you, Ryan. I've been brought up to hate you, but I always finish up admiring you. It's damned odd. Perhaps we should have been friends.'

'Perhaps we will be, but it might take a few years. Go to bed, Christy. Your face is starting to look quite puffy.'

'So is Rex's!' Christy said with satisfaction.

Rex began to smile. 'That's all right. Whatever else we are, we Langtons aren't dull.'

'How about promising me a return bout?' Christy said, wincing.

'You don't impress me, boy. Unlike some.'

Elizabeth moved stiffly to the door. 'The only way to handle this matter is to ignore it.'

'Honestly, Liz, you're priceless! It's good to see!' Rex took her elbow in the most courteous fashion. 'What about a little brandy?'

They were gone, and cautiously Christy took another look at his brother. He didn't know quite where he was, but Ryan looked his customary cool self. 'I'm sorry about that!' he said tentatively.

'I suggest you apologise to Kylie!' Ryan turned to him and his tone was icy.

Kylie's chin went up. The light caught her gleaming ivory skin and the sparkling jet of her eyes. 'Don't think I'm desperate for an apology from any one of you. And don't think you just have to say the word, Ryan Langton. I hate the lot of you! I hope you all hit the floor with a shattering crash. If I were a man I'd like to draw blood!'

'But, darling girl, I already require medication!' Christy said ruefully. 'All right, I'm off. Ryan is the only one you respect!'

There was utter quiet in the room after he had gone, then Kylie slid off the arm of the old wing-backed chair where she had come to rest because her legs were shaking so much. 'Goodnight!' she said wearily. 'I'm going to bed.'

'You do that!' Ryan returned quietly.

'Why you ever wanted me here I don't know. Your mother hates me.'

'You *do* create turmoil,' he agreed.

'Then find some way of getting me off the station. You're the Big Man. Pull another trick!'

He didn't answer but flicked the switch that plunged the room into darkness.

CHAPTER EIGHT

By mid-afternoon of the following day all of the guests had left the property except for Camilla, who had far too much to talk about with her friend and far too many plans to desert them. A barbecue had been arranged for lunch, but Kylie had deliberately avoided it, saddling up Domino mid-morning and not returning until she saw the Merrick Cessna dipping its wings over the homestead and flying off on its short trip home.

Poor Laura! she thought, looking up. Laura wasn't a woman of action when the only man in the world for her outside her father was Ryan. Between them, Camilla and her friends, Laura had been turned into a wallflower again. Laura's faith in her own ability to attract was such a newly fragile thing and Camilla was playing her hand just right. It was the first time Kylie had heard Elizabeth Langton call anyone 'a sweet girl'. If she had to decide herself, she would have voted for Laura, but Laura had so much money that perhaps she wouldn't have any worries anyway.

Many things were bothering Kylie that day. She knew now beyond any possible doubt that Mrs Langton disliked her, and yet she was sorry she had been provoked into saying such distressing, hurtful things. To bring up the past, and the intimate details of Elizabeth Langton's own life, was unforgivable. There was a time she had been kind to her, even if now

163

Elizabeth had accused her of being little more than an opportunist. Rich people were never fair.

Riding back to the compound she felt thoroughly drained. She would have to apologise for the unforgivable things she had said. She deeply regretted them. Despite Mrs Langton's hostility she had no right to make the terrible claim that Richard Langton had never loved his wife. It must have hurt and humiliated Elizabeth dreadfully, and Kylie's gilded skin burned with shame. How ever could she have said it? There was so much jealousy and intrigue in the family that somehow it had worn off on her. It had been said often of the Langton brothers that they wanted nothing but the land. Their wives simply provided them with sons and managed the domestic affairs of two great stations.

The land *was* a tremendous responsibility. It took hold of the mind and perhaps left a man with little time or passion for a woman. Richard Langton had been a hard man in a day of legendary hard men, his brother Gerald one of them. They had all feared and respected him, and her own father had often said that Elizabeth Langton, for all her wealth and position, had a very miserable time of it. The only human being who had ever truly entered Richard Langton's heart was his firstborn, Ryan. And God help me! Kylie thought miserably, he has touched me deeply as well. She could blind herself no longer to her true feelings, yet she couldn't wait to be off the property. She should never have come. There was no place for her here.

When she rode into the courtyard fronting on to

the home stables, Claudia and Camilla were standing idly, both immaculately turned out for riding. Kylie lifted her hand in greeting and was subjected to cool interested stares.

'Where have you been?' Claudia called. 'We missed you at lunch.'

'I had a headache. A ride always clears it.'

Claudia seemed to hesitate. 'I was thinking of giving Cam a few riding lessons. Like to help?'

Kylie was so surprised she felt like going to pieces, but instead she dismounted and Andy, the aboriginal attendant, came running out to take the big black.

'Thanks, Andy!' she smiled at him.

'Pleasure, missy!'

He led the horse away and Kylie walked across to join the older girls. 'I'd be pleased to help if you think I could.'

'Well, you do have a knack!' Claudia admitted almost grudgingly. 'Having an expert on the spot is an asset, and it's essential that Cam learns to ride!'

'Can't you guess why?' Camilla's veiled, alert eyes met Kylie's and she forced a smile but didn't answer. Camilla's short hair was like honey about her face and she had invested in a lovely outfit that moulded her slender figure.

No woman in her right mind would consider marrying a Langton, Kylie thought bleakly, and least of all Ryan. The trap was richly gilded, only women were too vulnerable and Camilla looked flushed, very animated and what was more telling, prepared and anxious to learn how to ride. Hitherto she had been notoriously shy of horses.

'What about Philanta for a mount?' Claudia was asking carelessly.

'Unsuitable!'

'*I* don't think so!' Claudia returned in her educated drawl.

'Surely it's too highly mettled for a beginner!' Kylie said evenly. 'You've been riding since you were a child. Philanta would be unsuitable for a beginner all her life, I should think.'

'Well, there's the problem!' Claudia said shortly. 'Most of our horses are pure bred. Ryan demands high mettle.'

'Then we'll have to use one of the workhorses,' Kylie said patiently. 'They're experienced and quiet.'

'What about that beautiful thing you were riding?' asked the unsuspecting Camilla. 'It looked very stately and you're only a bit of a thing.'

'Domino? He's a stallion.'

'What's that supposed to mean?'

'A stallion is a potentially dangerous animal,' Kylie explained. 'No beginner would ever be safe on one. Are you certain you want to start the lesson right now?'

'For God's sake don't discourage her!' Claudia burst out with more than a touch of heat.

'Forgive me, I don't mean to do that, only it's important she has the right mount. You should have spoken to Ryan.'

Camilla coloured like a schoolgirl, looking ravishingly pretty while she was at it. 'But I don't want him to know anything about it. It's going to be a *surprise*!'

'Well, all of the animals here are too volatile!' Kylie

said ironically. 'I'll get one of the boys to bring up a work horse from the yards.'

'I suggest we use Philanta,' Claudia broke in in a businesslike tone. 'I've never known her to give trouble.'

'Then I'll have to leave the lesson to you!' Kylie said, and meant it. 'I don't want the responsibility. In any case, you probably have a different method.'

Claudia's eyes were so cold she looked astonishingly like her mother. 'I'm sorry I asked!' she said, drawing up her tall, slim body.

'We—ell!' Kylie could hear her own voice faltering. 'I can only give you my opinion for what it's worth. I wouldn't like to see Camilla come to any harm.'

Camilla's peal of laughter rang in their ears. 'That's wonderful! Do you *mean* it? No worries, dear. I'm a quick learner once I put my mind to it!'

'I would rather you waited for another mount. If you don't want Ryan to know, Jeff would be very happy to help you.'

Claudia was furious, and she flung back her long flowing hair. 'Are you suggesting *I* can't?'

Kylie drew in her breath and countered the frosty blue eyes. 'I think you're forgetting how difficult a thing it is to learn how to ride properly. The right mount will make a tremendous difference and give Camilla confidence. I know Philanta is well trained and beautifully behaved in experienced hands, but in no way is she suitable for Camilla.'

Always an autocrat, Claudia glared back. 'I'll be the judge of that! You trust me, don't you, Cam?'

'Well, maybe not!' Camilla said at last, then laughed. 'Sure I do. I'm only interested in good-looking animals anyway. Let's get started. I'm going to master this no matter what. Perhaps little Miss Kylie here doesn't want me to shine in that direction?'

'On the contrary!' Kylie brushed her fingers through her tousled curls. 'I was prepared to take you seriously. It's you who's not listening to me. You can do without good looks at the beginning.'

'And don't expect us to listen!' Claudia broke out in her wrath. 'I tell you, I *know* Philanta. She's sensible, sweet-natured and mature. Also, she's the least volatile animal we have in at the moment. Anyone would think I was suggesting we put her up on Storm Boy. Come on, Cam!' she turned away to her silent friend. 'You've always been a quick learner in everything, and it's *so* important!'

Kylie gave up with a weary little gesture. 'Then you'll excuse me!'

She turned away and Claudia called after her:

'Thanks for nothing!'

A moment later Kylie heard Claudia calling out for Andy. It was inevitable that she would get her own way. Andy might agree that Philanta was too mettlesome, but he would do as he was told—there was no other way for an employee. Claudia was an experienced horsewoman and completely fearless. Perhaps Philanta would tolerate having a novice up on her back. Claudia always did and always would do as she pleased. It was impossible to restrain her and opposition only increased her obstinacy. The greater her arrogance, the greater the risk to Camilla. Elizabeth had really spoiled her daughter rotten. Still, Kylie wished them all the luck in the world. She just didn't want to be around.

There was a peculiar weight over her heart and she realised she didn't feel free to walk away. She loathed stupidity, and Claudia was being an arrogant little fool at her friend's expense. It was better to say goodbye to the lot of them and go home to peace and Sara's undemanding friendship. It wasn't a tragedy to fall in love. The tragedy was that she hadn't suspected it until now.

Birds were chattering in the avenue of trees and she kept moving down the narrow lane with a kind of stubborn resolution. She had to apologise to Mrs Langton, then, most painful of all, say goodbye to Ryan. Life went on and one had to survive. Hadn't Ryan taught her that, that night on Djangga? She had really fallen in love with him then, only her twisted memories had kept her in prison. Her father's death was the terrible consequence of not obeying an order. She could think of this sombrely now, and with detachment. He had thought to subdue the brutish instincts of a rogue and in the end it had destroyed him. *She* had been the real victim and she had condemned Ryan for years because of her intense shock. In truth she loved him, and it too was a calamity.

A breathless scream rent the air, hugely magnified to Kylie's appalled mind. She turned back in alarm, and it was this that saved her. Philanta was galloping like a rocket towards her, intoxicated by panic, completely out of control. Even through the long tremors that ran over her body Kylie was fascinated by the beauty of its flight. The gleaming chestnut coat was shot through with sunlight, mane and tail flying, striking legs and gleaming hooves spewing up fallen leaves and gravel.

There was no time to do anything, make motions or shout: 'Whoa!' She could do nothing to slacken that savage pace and Philanta was gaining on her with beautiful, sinewy, frightening grace. Through her mind flashed images of a figure lying prone on the sand. Directly over that figure were wild, thrashing legs. In a moment she would hear the sound of the shot. The whirling trees above her were shot through with a greeny gold light. It even seemed strange she had never lost her nerve with a horse before. She hadn't lost it now, but movement seemed vain. Philanta's immense power was filling her mind...

Voices were shouting and in the next minute she felt herself snatched up in a vicious lunge and hurled with her assailant over the low wall that bordered one side of the lane. Arms like steel cords were bound securely around her. They went skimming downhill together, rolling a long way until the railed fence rose up before them. Kylie felt him thrust her head down against his chest, then they slammed into the post and she heard the ominous crack to his head.

His arms dropped away from her instantly. She rolled over and sat up, flashing him one emotion-laden look:

'Ryan!'

He was lying on his back unconscious and she struggled across to him and placed his head tenderly in her lap. His skin was pale under the heavy tan and she put her head down in fright, rubbing her tear-stained cheek against his own. He seemed strangely young with the commanding expression wiped clear of his face, the startlingly blue eyes hidden. For a moment the thick fall of his hair obscured his bruised temple and when she wiped it clear, her colour ebbed even more. She started to tremble like a leaf in a gale, glad that the others were rushing downhill to get to them.

Christy reached her first, speaking with harsh urgency: 'You all right, Kylie?'

'It's Ryan!' She lifted her tragic little face and the intensity of her gaze would have melted a stone. 'He's cracked his head badly.'

Christy seemed to reel a little, then he dropped down beside his brother. Ryan's right temple was already discoloured, bleeding and swollen. 'He's out cold!' he said, and drew a long gasping breath. 'You can thank your lucky stars you're still alive, girl. I've never seen anyone move as fast as Ryan. I wouldn't have believed it, only I was an eye-witness. What were you trying to do, sacrifice yourself?'

She gave an agitated little gesture. 'I never wanted Ryan to be the sacrifice!'

'He went straight for you, without thinking. There wasn't time.'

'He looks so *young*!' she said in a pained whisper.

'He looks like Dad the day he died!' Christy burst out of his disruptive thoughts. 'God, we can't do without Ryan!'

'Well?' Jeff reached them next, settling himself on his haunches beside his prone brother. 'That's worse than I thought!'

The girls were beside them, Andy the stable boy and Ryan's foreman, Matt Taylor, a squat, powerfully built man with the habit of command. 'It probably isn't as bad as it looks.' He leaned down to satisfy himself no other damage had been done. 'You all right, ma'am?'

'I think so,' Kylie said shakily.

'You'd better put your head down,' Jeff murmured. 'You're paper-white!'

The tremble in Claudia's voice accurately told of her shock. 'If anything happens to him I'll never forgive myself. Kylie told me about Philanta, but I wouldn't listen!'

'Oh, shut up, Claud!' Jeff returned shortly. 'All your sins are forgiven.'

'What are we going to do about Ryan?' Kylie turned to Matt at her shoulder.

He moved in on her purposefully. 'I've already yelled for the jeep. We'll get him up to the house. That looks pretty ugly—I'd like the Doc to check it.'

'You murderous little bitch!' Christy said wildly, looking up at his sister's drawn face. 'You love to have it all your own way. For pity's sake, couldn't you have used a little sense?'

'I'm just as angry with myself!' she said quietly, and started to cry.

Camilla put a hand around her. 'That's a terrible thing to say to your sister!'

'Do you think I care?' Christy cried emotionally. 'What do you think she's in for when Mother hears?'

'Oh, shut up, the lot of you!' Matt said explosively. 'He's coming around. There can't be a human being in the world who hasn't made a mistake—remember that, young feller. Your sister has had one hell of a fright, not to speak of the rest of us.'

'Even I should be hoppin' mad!' Camilla said

presently. 'Bucked right out of the saddle!'

Ryan made the faintest moaning sound and Kylie bit her lip, settling him more comfortably. There were no tears in her eyes now, but they made dusky tracks down her face.

Matt clasped a hand round Ryan's shoulder. 'How is it, Boss?' Ryan didn't respond and he added under his breath, 'God, you can crack a man's head like a nut!'

'Half a minute!' Ryan groaned. 'I can believe that!' He stared up at Kylie with intense, puzzled concentration. 'Don't I know you?'

'I'm terribly, terribly sorry!' she said, and started to cry again.

His face relaxed and he reached up a hand. 'What the hell were you playing at?'

'Don't ever bother to save me again!' She caught his hand and carried it to her mouth, uncaring that they were all watching.

'Let me help you up,' Matt said anxiously. The densely blue eyes had lost their impersonal expression, but they still lacked their usual brilliant clarity.

'Right!' Ryan seemed to apply himself to the task.

A spasm crossed Claudia's face and she started to wail. 'It's all my fault!'

'I expect it is!' Ryan said as though it amused him. 'You've been over-long learning a lesson. Is Cam all right?'

'One bruised posterior!' said Camilla, leaning over him. 'I can help you, can't I, Ryan?'

'He's got us men, hasn't he?' Christy asked irritably, obviously shaken to see his brother in pain.

'If you'll kindly stop fighting over the honour of

assisting me, I'll get up!' Ryan said in a crisp, authoritative tone. 'Stay with me, Kylie. I don't want to lose you. I'm in no shape for a repeat performance.'

'It was the sun in my eyes. It blinded me.' Her great eyes sparkled like jets and he stared at her with disconcerting thoroughness.

'Remember when I took my first spill, Matt?' Ryan groped for Matt's strong arm, put pressure on it and stood up a little groggily, then after a minute relinquished his hold.

'Sure!' Matt said soothingly. 'You were about eight years old—a tough guy even then!'

'I had Dad to think about,' Ryan said with amused irony. 'He didn't believe in even the youngest child crying.'

'Don't say that!' said Claudia, distressed with her mental pictures.

'It doesn't stop it from being true. I spent all my childhood being the sort of person Dad wanted.'

'Don't think of it!' Kylie said quietly, and he raised his eyebrow at her.

'I should like you to, even if it isn't any use!' He shut his eyes briefly and winced.

'You have a clear recollection of everything that happened, haven't you, Boss?'

'*Too* clear!' Ryan retorted dryly. 'Kylie, you bother me!'

She came to stand beside him and took his hand. 'I'm sorry. I know I'm saying it too late.'

'You've got tears in your eyes,' he said lightly. 'Why?'

'I'm funny sometimes.'

'You are indeed!'

'The jeep's coming!' Jeff checked and turned his head. 'We'll get you up to the house. Claudia, instead of standing about looking so penitent, why don't you call up the doc?'

Claudia's voice had lost all its characteristic self-assurance. She sounded as painfully bewildered as a child. 'I just want you all to know I'm very, very sorry. I should have listened to you, Kylie. I will the next time!' She glanced at Kylie so appealingly that Kylie smiled at her in a funny kind of wonder. Pain was moving across her own brow. When she got up to the house she was certain she was going to be sick.

Kylie lay quietly in the semi-darkness, savouring a new-found calmness. Doctor Stephens had flown in an hour before and pronounced Ryan indestructible, though even so he had to rest quietly for a little while. Once she was sure of the doctor's verdict, Kylie had retired, leaving Ryan to the care of his family. Claudia, with most unaccustomed solicitude, had brought her a couple of aspirins and apologised again for the 'pig-headedness' that could have had such dreadful results. After that, Kylie had thrown off the beautiful brocade bedspread and lay down on her bed. Shock often made people see things more clearly and Claudia for the first time in her life seemed doubtful of her own behaviour. Christy hadn't spared her either. He had been appallingly frank.

Kylie heaved herself up on to the pillows and shook her head as if to clear it. Mrs Langton had greeted them heavily with strain on her face. In the telling she had had to realise that Ryan had placed himself in danger for Kylie's sake, but nothing in her manner

implied blame on anyone's part. It did not occur to
her to allow a scene to flourish, though it had been
useless preventing Christy from having his say. Elizabeth had said nothing, although Kylie considered her
very quietness was a cloak for more volatile feelings.

The knock on her door was so muffled Kylie
scarcely heard it. Tentatively she called a 'come in'
and was surprised to see Mrs Langton on the thres-
hold. Kylie moved off the bed and stood up. 'Is there
something you want, Mrs Langton?'

'To speak to you, my dear!' Elizabeth said gravely.
'May I?'

'Of course!'

Kylie indicated a chair and waited until the older
woman took a seat, the pale blue eyes making little
sweeps around the room, touching on the photograph
Kylie always carried with her: her mother and father
laughing into the sun, with her, a toddler with a head
full of curls clutching a huge panda. Without that
photograph it had often seemed to Kylie she had
never had a family at all. But there was the evidence,
and it was a lovely photograph.

Elizabeth's eyes didn't soften or register sympathy
and Kylie burst out jerkily: 'Please let me apologise
for the unforgivable things I said last night. I had no
right!'

'No, you didn't!' Elizabeth confirmed briefly. 'However, if this is to be the moment of truth, many of the
things you said *were* true. I'm sure you'll forgive me
my humiliation.'

There was a crackle in her voice that was all too
obvious and Kylie looked away. 'I do, and I understand it. Hostility and rejection have always made *me*

miserable. You see, Mrs Langton, I'm out of my environment on Sovereign River. I always have been.'

'I'm glad you're aware of it!' Elizabeth said thoughtfully. 'I know I could have been kinder to you.'

'You *were* when I was a child.'

It was Elizabeth's turn to let her eyes slide away. 'Claudia told me what really happened. You should have remained to assist her. She's really very headstrong!'

Kylie answered with a nod of her head. 'That she can learn from it is what's important. I'm glad I was able to make my peace with you, Mrs Langton, before I go. Doctor Stephens has offered to fly me out in the morning. I can pick up another flight at Longreach.'

Apparently she had said the right thing, for Elizabeth's cold, handsome face brightened. 'Then may I wish you a good night's sleep and a good trip home. You're a clever girl, Kylie, and you have style. I'm sure you'll make a good future for yourself. You must remember to let us have word of you.'

'Naturally!' Kylie managed a cool little smile of her own. 'I would never have forgiven myself if Ryan had been hurt in any way.'

The bitter blue eyes flew to Kylie's face. 'You love him, don't you?'

Kylie didn't even bother to deny it, though she knew it might be disastrous. She was no match for Elizabeth Langton anyway. 'You're not mistaken. I *do* love him. I suppose I always did, but Ryan is a whole world away from me.'

'All the same,' Elizabeth said, more kindly, 'I believe he cares about your welfare. He's always taken his duties seriously. I shall suggest he makes you a bigger allowance.'

'That's not at all necessary!' Kylie returned swiftly. 'There's nothing more I could possibly want of him. It's not likely I'll ever forget he risked his life twice for me!' She found she had reached such an acute state of tension that she jumped to her feet, and Mrs Langton was obliged to stand up.

'You seem upset, dear. You've had a shock and you're still very pale. I'll have a tray sent up to your room. Ryan is resting quietly. There are no definite signs of concussion, but I don't want him disturbed. I expect it will be very tiresome for him, but he's going to have a lot of nurses. It's so rarely we get to make a fuss of him. Poor little Camilla was very much affected!'

Kylie didn't speak, feeling quite weaponless. Elizabeth Langton would be a very unscrupulous woman where her son was concerned. Elizabeth walked to the door, a faint flush on her strong cheekbones. 'Let us both forget what we said to one another, and don't be too proud to accept a bigger allowance from Ryan. Young girls need so much more money these days for dressing, and I imagine you have lots of admirers!'

Kylie lifted her eyes, a faint grimness in her own expression. 'It's kind of you to think of me, Mrs Langton, but I'm quite happy. *Under the circumstances*. Please believe I meant my apology sincerely.'

Elizabeth dismissed it with a turn of her thin, elegant hand. 'The best thing for you would be an early night. You're all eyes. Really you haven't changed much at all since you were a child. George is leaving quite early, I believe, so I may not see you again. Every good wish for your future, Kylie. You're the most remarkable young girl I've ever known!'

And you're a scheming, hard, possessive woman! Kylie thought in her pain. She couldn't say it, so she smiled, meeting Elizabeth Langton's eyes directly.

Whatever Elizabeth recognised in that dark gaze, she withdrew abruptly and Kylie sank down into her chair again. Had she really expected anything else? She had known for a long time that she wasn't wanted on Sovereign River, merely tolerated. Camilla, Laura, all the others, what did they really know about the sort of mother-in-law they seemed anxious to get? Kylie understood everything and she was an outsider, with no chance of belonging. The only thing she could do was break the connection.

She stood up and moved quickly to the huge red cedar wardrobe, her teeth set together tightly to stop herself from crying. She threw her dresses and riding clothes on to the bed, then pulled out her suitcase. There was no time for tears, she had things to do!

CHAPTER NINE

WEEKS went by, then a couple of months. Kylie heard twice from Christy, had an unexpected card from Claudia at Christmas time and a large cheque from Ryan which Sara had immediately grabbed and insisted they splurge on a big, beautiful holiday on Paradise Island, the most luxurious resort on the fabulous Great Barrier Reef. Kylie hadn't objected, for Sara was only trying to be kind. It was obvious that she had gone right back into her shell and it was Sara's solution to get her away. One had to stand by one's friends, and it was Sara's nature to take some constructive course of action.

Oddly enough Kylie recovered in a way, because, surrounded as she was by so much peace and glorious scenery, it seemed easier to cope with her insoluble dilemma. Sara made her drag herself out of her apathy anyway and they swam and sunbathed, played tennis and golf, peered through glass-bottomed boats at the exquisite, incredible world of coral, hunted up shells, and at night joined in the dancing and fun. Sara met a young man she fell frantically in love with and Kylie met no one at all. There could be only one man in her life, and he called himself Ryan Langton. The years seemed to loom endlessly before her to discipline her feelings, and she had to clutch at her pride.

Once they returned to teaching, it was easy to fill the days with work, but with the night came dreams to torment her. She could never eradicate Ryan from her mind, the emotional ties were too strong. Sara, however, was supremely happy and though she regretted what she called 'abandoning' Kylie, Timothy was always there wanting to take her out. Sometimes Kylie had the energy to make up a foursome and join them, sometimes not. She was Ryan's and she would be for as long as she lasted.

She was too thin, and as Sara was dining out so often she didn't make much of the evening meal and the nights she had lectures the very thought of food made her ill. It was Friday again and she faced the weekend on her own. Sara had taken Timothy up to meet her parents and although she had invited Kylie and sincerely wanted her to join them Kylie considered it would be better if she stayed at home. Nora Anthony's kind eyes would spot her problem immediately and she would put food before her that she simply couldn't refuse. Besides, even the kindest, well-meaning probing hurt her.

When the doorbell rang, she couldn't think who on earth it would be. Sara hadn't dated anyone but Timothy for weeks and Mark had disappeared out of her own life in a resentful huff. Her newly washed hair stood silkily about her delicate face and she was only wearing her robe. It was impossible to ignore the continuing peal of the bell, so she went to the door, determining on keeping it barely ajar on the safety chain. Very occasionally they had had the irritation of after-hours salesmen, but she had to be certain just who it was.

Later she wondered why she hadn't fainted. As it was she just barely found her voice. '*Ryan*!'

He looked handsome and mocking in the old remembered way, looming above her. 'I approve of the safety catch, Kylie, but only for strangers. Let me in!'

She found it difficult to slip the lock. This had happened some time before and he repeated her name as if to awaken her from her little trance. At last the door was open and she let him inside. She wasn't even controlled enough to ask him a sensible question. She just stood there staring, and he took her hand and pulled her across the carpet and into a chair.

'It's really me!' he said gently.

She recognised everything about him, his head and his dark profile, the lean arrogant body, but she wouldn't meet his eyes. Her heart was beating so violently it felt like a bird quivering inside her. 'Why?' she asked faintly.

'Surely I'm allowed to call on my ward?' He moved into the deep comfort of an armchair, his blue eyes flicking over her.

'But there's absolutely no need!' She didn't know it, but she was wringing her hands together. 'You do your duty beautifully from a distance!'

'That sounds like you!' he taunted her. 'What have you been doing to yourself? You're all big eyes and delicate bones!'

'Working. Studying!' she said stiltedly, her profile like a head on a cameo. 'I don't have much free time.'

'Where's Sara?' he looked about him with interest, noting one or two changes in decor.

'Off to her parents for the weekend. She's fallen in love with a very nice young man, now she wants her parents' approval.'

'I thought Sara was a very marriage-minded young lady. Now I see I wasn't mistaken!'

'Naturally!' she said shortly. 'Pretty nearly everything you think is right!'

'I'll grant you that, Kylie. Would you stop pulling at that wrap? I know what you look like.'

'Well, it's not what you're used to!' she flashed.

'Oh, for God's sake, you're not talking about that charmer, Camilla?' he queried, and gave a faint laugh.

'You'll notice I'm not making inquiries about anyone,' she said.

'Because you're feeling sorry for yourself?'

'On the contrary, I want to keep them at a safe distance.' She felt detestably vulnerable in her thin robe, her hair standing silkily like a child's all round her face. 'I thought I'd be on my own!' she said a little impatiently. 'I've just washed my hair.'

'And it doesn't look too bad at all. We're going out anyway,' he said firmly. 'You look as if you could do with a good dinner.'

'Are you trying to say *gaunt*?'

'An unlikely descriptive word, Kylie!' His head was thrown back and his blue eyes were gleaming. 'No, a delicate porcelain beauty will do!'

She drew a quick little breath and pulled the silk crêpe-de-chine still closer around her so that it moulded every inch of her rather than disguised the singing line of her body. The table lamp beside her threw shadowed hollows into her cheeks and plum lights into her shining hair. 'It was good of Christy to write!' she said suddenly with almost ludicrous urgency, his presence was so distracting her. 'I had a card from Claudia at Christmas time. By the way, thank you for the cheque. Sara and I had a holiday on Paradise Island.'

'Yes, I know.'

'How?' She stared across at him as if he were in league with the devil.

'A friend of mine owns it.'

'Oh, I *see*!' she said fiercely. 'That's nothing new!'

'There aren't all that many Kylies about.'

'There *must* be!' she said as if she were suffocating. 'You like checking up, don't you?'

'I'd find you in any corner of the world,' he told her. 'That's just the way it is!'

She looked pointedly across at the carved cabinet they used as a bar. 'May I offer you something? Maybe you'd prefer tea, or coffee?'

'Don't bother!' he said negligently. 'I intend to feed you before I try to talk any sense to you. The long weeks have reduced you to a pixie!'

'What's the occasion?' she asked curtly.

'Let's say it pleases me,' he answered with arrogant simplicity. 'Go and put on your prettiest dress.'

A little glitter of antagonism shone in her eyes. 'You haven't changed a bit, have you? Still giving orders?'

'And half of you still fighting them?'

His eyes raked her so unmercifully she jumped to her feet as if a demon was after her, tripping ignominiously on Sara's colourful, handwoven rug. 'Damn, damn, damn!' she wailed.

'My poor little girl!' His arms were around her in an instant, binding her silken body to him.

'Let me go!' It seemed important she fight him, and for a moment her whole body shook in a passionate agony of resentment. She had him one day and the next he was gone. He was cruel, and he knew perfectly well what he was doing to her.

His breath touched her cheek. 'Kylie darling, don't fight me, you're breaking my heart!'

'You haven't got one!'

'I *do*!' He twisted her around to him and she began to moan softly. The blood and the skin and the nerves had a wild life of their own. 'I wasn't going to do this,' he muttered, his voice rough edged with curbed violence. The next second he lifted her into his arms and walked with her to the sofa.

Her wrap had fallen back to reveal the little slip nightdress beneath it, but it didn't seem to matter. She had lain in his arms before and she had only been fifteen years old. She should curse it for ever, because she had begun to love him as a woman from then. Shivers were running through her like arrowheads of flame. It no longer seemed important to hold on to her pride. She wanted him with such a profound hunger that when he bent his head she opened her mouth to receive his hard kiss, her arms wrapping themselves about him as though she couldn't bear to let him go. Whichever way he chose to treat her she knew very well she was asking for it. Ryan was her downfall, her love, her calamity.

'Love me!' she whispered fiercely. 'It's been terrible without you!'

'I'm glad you couldn't stand it!' The harsh discipline he kept on himself was being lost in a riot of excitement and the scent of her body. Her eyes were tightly closed and the heavy lashes were wet. He lifted his dark head for a moment to look at her and the colour in his eyes was quite startling. 'What are you crying about?'

'Does it matter?'

'Naturally you'll never tell me!'

'What do you want to hear?' She opened her eyes and they were brilliant, flooded with feeling. 'That I love you so much, I could die of it!'

'Say it again!' His caressing hands became so urgent she gave a distinct tremble of shock and he bent and kissed the curve of her breast. 'I wanted to do that when you were barely sixteen.'

'You can't mean it!' she whispered.

'I really did. My God!'

She looked up at him helplessly. 'I have nothing to say.'

'No matter. I can make love to you now!'

'And then you'll leave me, find some excuse and fly away.'

'Don't move!' he said, and threaded his fingers through her hair. 'You and I are a team.'

'But it can't be!'

'Why not?' He tightened his hold. 'You love me. I think you did when you were just a wild and lonely little girl.'

'But there are others!'

'That's true!' He laughed quietly. 'One or two have found you particularly attractive!'

'I mean your mother!' she said in distress. 'She'll never recognise me.'

He slipped his hand down over her shoulder to cup her tender breast. 'I can't believe anyone would be foolish enough to reject my wife!'

'I doubt if you know what you're saying. Are you asking me to marry you?'

'No. I'm telling you!' His other hand was repeating the caressing motion until the blood pounded in her ears.

'Stop it!' she pleaded. 'I can't think properly!'

'Do you want to?' His voice was husky, and he lifted her hard up against him, his hand slipping to the small of her back, his mouth warm in the cleft between her breasts.

Her whole body felt boneless ... weightless ... and she heard him repeating over and over her name.

'Kylie!'

It aroused a storm of emotion in her, both tender and violent. She was no longer a young girl but a woman exulting in her own power, a Delilah with his thick, heavy hair beneath her hands. She arched her body in a slow deliberate way, seeking his mouth. 'This is how it is,' she said softly. 'I love you. Whatever you choose to do. I'll accept it.'

Involuntarily his blood thickened and he caught her mouth violently, with such a strong ruthless desire her skin turned a startling white. Kylie twisted her head a little and he checked as though he could feel her accelerated heart rate. The tumultuous intensity gave way to a deep tenderness impossible to describe, a heavy, drugged sweetness that melted her bones.

It was heaven itself to be wanted, to feel this one man's driving need. She clung to him in enchantment, revelling in the weight of his hard body, his physical hold over her, that was turning her into a breathless, vital thing, wanting more, always more...

Ryan set her free so abruptly, her mind refused to accept the loss. He was sitting up and she could only gaze up at him in shock.

'What's wrong?' she asked.

'Nothing, baby!' He bent and kissed her mouth gently. 'You're all I'll ever want, but I can wait. I've had plenty of practice!'

She made a desperate attempt to match his control, and he smiled at her and stood up. 'Every inch of your body is tinted with colour!'

'D-d-d-do you still want to go out?' she stammered.

'I'll say I do. Get up and get dressed!' He leaned forward and threw her her wrap.

'Does your mother know you're here?'

Unexpectedly he burst out laughing. 'God, what a question! I'm thirty-four years old.'

'That's just what I mean. Your mother's had you for all that time. She'll never take kindly to any kind of daughter-in-law, let alone *me*!'

His blue eyes were brilliant, amused and tender. 'Mamma knows I'm here and why I'm here. Does that answer your question?'

'She must be very unhappy.'

'Not at all. I think she's planning a big wedding and after that she and Claudia are going to Europe. It's Claud's turn for the Grand Tour.'

Kylie stood up rather shakily and thrust her arms into the sleeves of her robe. 'I can't believe it!'

'Don't brood about it,' he told her. 'It was no trick at all. Of course mothers get a little peculiar at times, but when I told her my love for you was total and unalterable, she offered to arrange everything. It was no revelation, believe me. My mother will never destroy my love and respect for her, and when you think about it, Kylie, she deserves a little compassion. My father must have been one of the hardest men in the whole wide world.'

'If she'd let me I'd like to offer her *my* affection, but she won't!'

'It will all work out in time, Kylie. My mother will come to be as proud of you as I am. Any girl as beautiful and cultivated as you are can take her place anywhere. My mother knows it—don't think she doesn't. It might even comfort you to know she respects you. Some women take hold of a man's mind, and you're one of them. My mother admitted she feared your strong influence, but she didn't make enough allowances for your tender heart. You're not like anybody else. You're a miracle, and it's your turn to be happy now. I thought that was what you wanted?'

'I couldn't bear it if you came to resent me!' she

cried convulsively, and hurled herself at him. 'It's *you* I care about. I can't come between you and your family. Take me if you like, and finish it!'

'Little fool!' He shook her and there was an explosive dynamism in his touch. 'You're going to be my wife! Got it? What the hell do I care about sexual dalliance? You're the one woman in the world I want. It hurts me to hear you talk like that. You've got to learn to trust me. I'll always look after you. There's no life without love in it, and I've loved you for a long time.'

'And I used to make such stupid vengeful little plans about you!' she whispered, and rested against his chest.

'Well, yes, but it doesn't seem to have made any difference. I still want you, and no one will ever hurt you as long as I live!'

A tremor passed through her to him. She lifted herself on tiptoes and smiled into his brilliant eyes.

'I love you, Ryan. You're going to hear it until the world sinks!'

Confidence was born in her that moment that no one would ever take away. If Ryan loved her she could be anything he wanted; *do* anything he wanted. Let him make love to her with the ravishing, mind-toppling sensuality only she could invite; bear his children, charm his family, run his household, even win over his mother. She would even stand beside him on Melbourne Cup day radiant and triumphant in the winner's circle. She could see it all clearly. She could do anything for Ryan. She felt astonishingly alive.

'Go and dress!' he said as though it was killing him to push her away. 'We're going out to celebrate!'

Harlequin
Announces the
COLLECTION
EDITIONS
OF 1978

Harlequin's Collection 1?
ANDREA BLAKE
Night of the Hurrica

Harlequin's Collection 106   1.25
ANNE WEALE
If This Is Love

stories of special
beauty and significance

25 Beautiful stories of particular merit

In 1976 we introduced the first 100 Harlequin Collections — a selection of titles chosen from our best sellers of the past 20 years. This series, a trip down memory lane, proved how great romantic fiction can be timeless and appealing from generation to generation. Perhaps because the theme of love and romance is eternal, and, when placed in the hands of talented, creative, authors whose true gift lies in their ability to write from the heart, the stories reach a special level of brilliance that the passage of time cannot dim. Like a treasured heirloom, an antique of superb craftsmanship, a beautiful gift from someone loved, — these stories too, have a special significance that transcends the ordinary.

Here's your 1978 Harlequin Collection Editions . . .